BLOW YOURSELF AWAY

Turn Blowjobs Into a
Mind-Blowing Experience
For Yourself.

*A Gay Sexpert's Guide
For Women*

MICHAEL ALVEAR

WOODPECKER**MEDIA**

Praise For Blow Yourself Away

"Who better to give sex advice to straight women than a gay man? ... Empowers women to think about what pleasuring a man can mean for their own pleasure ... most successful when it's presenting facts and solutions, which provides a nice balance to its cheeky innuendos."

—Kirkus Reviews

"Ladies, the balls are in your court! With Michael as your penis coach—and a winning strategy that places your pleasure up front and center— you've got game and then some."

—Ian Kerner, PhD LMFT, sex therapist and NY Times best-selling author of *She Comes First*

"Alvear beautifully reframes what has generally been considered a "job" into a sexually satisfying activity for women. Filled with laugh-out-loud humor, sharp insights and powerful advice. A great addition to the canon of sex self-help."

—Dr. Sadie Allison, Founder TickleKitty.com and Bestselling Author, *Tickle His Pickle*

"In *Blow Yourself Away*, author Michael Alvear helps women identify their urges, whet their own appetites and then encourage the feminine instinct toward pleasure. This book is a witty guide to showing women how to enjoy men."

—Mama Gena, Founder, School of Womanly Arts

Table Of Contents

Introduction

Raise your hand if you're wondering what a gay man like me can teach a straight woman like you about oral sex.

Now, slap yourself with that hand and ask for a refund because I don't want anybody that naive reading my Pulitzer Prize-winning copy. *Of course* I can teach you a lot, not just because I'm gay (hello! I don't just *have* a penis, I *like* them, too!) but because of what I do for a living.

I've been writing a gay sex advice column called *Need Wood? Tips For Getting Timber* for the last twelve years. I got started when an editor at a gay magazine asked if I'd like to write a funny, informative sex column. "Sure," I said. "Send me your cutest employees and I'll get started."

That led to a book called *Men Are Pigs But We Love Bacon*, and ultimately a co-hosting gig on *The Sex Inspectors*, a heterosexual TV show that aired on Britain's Channel 4 and America's HBO. I got the role because of my answer to the final question on the screen test: "What do you think of women who fake their orgasms?"

"Not much," I said. *"Men can fake whole relationships."*

But enough about me. Let's talk about you. If you're like most women, you're giving what I call "Canadian blowjobs." You know, well meaning but dull. Not just for him, but for you.

That's about to stop. Because with this book I'm going to show you how to give the kind of head that'll get you married or promoted. Raise your hand if that last sentence offended you. Now, slap yourself...okay, that's getting redundant. My point, and I do have one, is that this isn't going to be a dry, boring, tedious roundup of BJ banter. It's going to be a politically incorrect, no-holds-barred romp that's going to leave you locked, cocked and ready to rock your man.

More importantly it's going to do what no other book on the subject has done: Show you how to enjoy a hard penis <u>on your terms</u>; to discover the joys of your partner's genitals without feeling pressured to do or act in ways that aren't comfortable, comforting or sexually exciting. It's about appreciating the strength, length, width and hardness of an erect cock because of what it can do for you, not for what you can do to it.

Many women think that blowjobs are something you do *for* your partner. While you can get a lot of pleasure out of "giving," things can go sour if you lose or ignore your own urges and desires. I have a different proposition: Blowjobs are for you as much as they are for him. They shouldn't be a chore but a choice you make for your own pleasure.

I call my approach the "selfish blowjob" because it's more about you than him. Yes, of course, your partner will get a lot out of it, but his satisfaction, while necessary, is beside the point. It's your pleasure that matters.

Wait, how can that be? Blowjobs are for men! Women are

merely the vehicle to deliver them, no? Men receive the pleasure while women give it. It's like entertaining your in-laws. You don't do it because you want to; you do it because your partner wants you to. Plus, it's work! The blowjobs, I mean. Although you could make the same case for the in-laws.

Of course, not every woman dislikes blowjobs (or their in-laws). There are a growing number of women who absolutely love it (you go, girls!). And you're going to hear from lots of them later in the book. Through my years of writing sex advice columns I can tell you that the majority of women don't fall into "love it or hate it" camps. I could sum up their feelings in one word: *Meh.*

You can make giving blowjobs a peak sexual experience for yourself by understanding what an erect cock can do for you, not for what you can do to it.

The good news is that by the time you finish this book, you will have a completely different attitude (and aptitude!) about giving head.

I'm going to show you how to turn a *Meh* into a *Meow*. I'm going to show you how to think of it as a turn-on, not a turn-off. By the time I'm done you're going to be gagging for it (as opposed to on it). You're going to see blowjobs as an effective way for you to pleasure *yourself*, not just him.

In fact, this is what separates this book from all others on the subject. Learning techniques is fine—if all you want to be is a skilled worker. But to truly give great head, you have to see it as a critical to your own sexual satisfaction.

I'm not just going to show you the art of getting through giving. I'm going to show you something far more powerful: How to get so turned on by blowjobs that they become necessary for your sexual satisfaction. I'm going to show you that it's possible to like them so much that you will beg your partner to let you do it. Like this woman:

"I have no idea why but there are some days where I'm actually craving the feel of cock in my mouth and I basically need to persuade my boyfriend to let me do it. I think it's partially to do with his scent that he emits during sex."

—T.

You are going to hear from over forty different women on why they love giving blowjobs. Their stories and anecdotes come from blog posts, columns and discussion boards all over the Internet (especially Reddit. In fact, if the quote isn't directly sourced, it means it came from a Reddit thread).

Some quotes are informative, some are moving, some are shocking and some are funny. Put together you'll see a common theme: It is possible to turn a boring chore into a stellar choice. It is possible for women to like giving blow-jobs as much or more than the men receiving them.

Let's find out how you can, too. Your pleasure-mobile just pulled up and it's going to take you places you've only dreamed about. Hop in.

PUTTING HIS PENIS ON A PEDESTAL

Chapter One

Blowjobs: Turning Tasks Into Turn-Ons

"Personally, I absolutely LOVE oral sex. I have fun with it. I kiss it, nuzzle the base, rub my breasts against it, stroke the balls, lightly suck them, blow on the head, and generally just adore it. It's the enthusiasm that I put in to my blowjobs that make them fun.

—C.

You simply cannot give good head unless you see it as a way of satisfying your own sexual needs. You can have the best technique in the world but if you don't see it as an avenue to satisfying your own sexual pleasure, you'll just say things like, "Put it in my mouth, already. I got clothes to fold!"

Think back to the most memorable oral sex a man has ever performed on YOU. What do you remember most—that thing he did with his tongue or the feeling of getting sucked into a vortex of sexual energy that made you temporarily forget your name?

Let me make a few assertions about your memory of that session. That guy who went down on you? He LOVED doing it, didn't he? It wasn't just that he was good at it, he L-O-V-E-D licking and kissing you, the taste of you, the everything of you. Technique? Skills? Yes, I'm sure he was good, maybe even great. But that would have just made him a talented laborer. You have that searing memory because he was a passionate lover who loved going down on you. THAT'S what made him great and that's what's going to make you great at going down on your partner.

So the question becomes, how do you start seeing blowjobs as vehicles to your own pleasure (the way your guy did in that memory of yours)? How do you cultivate a love for penis? How can you start seeing it as a sex toy for your mouth? How do you get yourself to like blowjobs so much that you want to do it as much or more than your partner wants to have it?

It starts by seeing proof that other women are indeed turned on by blowjobs and not just because they like the effect it has on their men. Here's one of my favorite testimonials by an extremely perceptive and articulate woman on Reddit:

"I love blowjobs because:

1. *The epitome of his manhood is right there, right in front of me. I get an excellent view.*

12

2. *My face has much more heightened sensation than my vagina. I can see him, I can smell him, I can taste him, I can touch him with my hands, I can explore all of his contours and textures with my tongue, etc. The feeling of his cock pulsing in my mouth as he gives me his load ... None of the sensory stimulation of his cock is as heightened in the vagina as in the mouth (the vagina has the literal sexual stimulation, so it's not like I prefer one or the other).*

3. *I can more directly control his pleasure. Him being sexually stimulated is a huge mental turn-on for me—it doesn't give me literal sexual stimulation, but it's a big mental turn-on, and sex is half mental anyway.*

4. *If I'm on my period or I don't think I can take a pounding at the moment, they're a great way for me to still enjoy sexual contact.*

5. *Blowjobs are an act where I'm in control. I usually enjoy being quite submissive, but when I give a blowjob I'm the one doing all the work and controlling everything—he is surrendering his vulnerable manhood to my mouth, and I'm in control of it."*

—V.

13

Now *there* is a woman who's in touch with her sexuality! How can you get closer to her sensibility? By getting in touch with why you like penis in the first place and letting those thoughts SWELL to huge proportions. Let's take a look at some of those thoughts and why it would make sense to be turned on by giving a blowjob.

A Hard Dick Is A Powerful Symbol of Something You Love: Masculinity

You are attracted to maleness, strength and virility and nothing personifies these traits more than the erect cock. It's strong, it's hard and it commands you to surrender. Few things can put your femininity in stark relief to masculinity more than a hard penis. It is not just the staff of life but the stuff of dreams. Wet dreams. It epitomizes almost every aspect of masculinity: It's big, thick, hard, strong, muscled, driven, and, it must be said, without conscience.

If you like a man for being a man, then it's only natural to crave the symbol of his manhood. When you hold your partner's erect penis you should (hopefully) be in awe of its strength and want to feel its masculine prowess in every part of your body. His hard-on should give you a "wide-on!"

> "I love, love, love blowjobs. I would be perma-
> nently attached to a penis if I could. I just love
> 'em so much."
>
> —S.

"Cock is yummy! You hear that 'Merica?"

—R.

A Hard Dick Is Proof That You're Desirable

A penis gets hard when its owner spies a beautiful, desirable woman. Namely, you. Now if you're like most body-conscious women, you probably don't believe your partner when he says you have a beautiful body. You convict him of sexual perjury—lying to get laid.

You won't get an argument from me—men lie for sex. We practically carry business cards that say "Professional Liar." But there's a flaw in your logic. Yes, men will say anything to get laid. *To a woman he finds attractive.*

See, you have to understand something about men. We give our penises nicknames so we can be on a first-name basis with the person making all of our decisions. And while we lie to do Mr. Happy's bidding, Mr. Happy himself is incapable of lying.

It's really difficult for a man to get an erection for a woman he's not attracted to. Even Viagra, Levitra, and Cialis won't help. They won't work unless the man is turned on. They can open up the valves to let more blood into the penis, but they cannot make a man want you. You may be resentful at times of the penis's persistence or its alarming lack of conscience, but never, ever doubt its sincerity.

Knowing you can turn your partner on (look at that erection!) is the ultimate sexual compliment; a statement of your desirability. It's a sexualized electrical current with a feedback loop—he gets excited so you get excited. He sees your excitement and gets more excited. And soon you're both sucked into a vortex of desire.

But what is the outer manifestation of his desire? His hard cock. It's not only about you, it's *for* you. And that's why so many women want it more than the latest silicon rabbit.

A Hard Dick Is Your Chance To Be In Control & Exert Dominance

There is yet another way to fall in love with your partner's yogurt chucker and that is to understand how powerful his erection makes you. After all, his hardon is a response to your presence. YOU are eliciting this response from him. I don't know of a more convincing display of power than to completely own a man's attention, to change his physical, emotional and psychological state. You got him hard? You have him right where you want him. Well done!

So how do you dominate him if it's you pleasuring him? Because YOU decide how he's going to feel by where you place your hands. YOU decide how he is going to react when you put your warm moist mouth on his member. Again, he is reacting to what you're doing and that means you're in control. Revel in it like these women do:

"Blowing my partner makes me feel sexy and powerful because I can so completely control a man simply with my mouth and tongue. And afterwards, he (my man, at least) has a cute, tired smile on his face, and always wants a nice long cuddle-session."

—T.

"I love the sense of power that I have when I hold my man's cock in my mouth or hands. At that moment and for the next hour or two ... I am in control of what happens ... and I am responsible for him having the most sensational, meaningful experience possible."

—A. in www.literotica.com

"It makes me feel so sexy and powerful. I love to watch my guy while I give him a BJ, seeing the ecstasy on his face and knowing that I'm making that happen with my mouth—it feels awesome. Often by the time I've finished, I'm so turned on by HIM being turned on, I'll be wet and ready to go..."

—G.

"I love the emotional power I have over my partner in being able to dictate speed, bringing him to the edge, stopping ... having him scream, beg, or moan. And either letting things calm down and begin again, or bringing things

to a head. It's TOTAL control, one that you decide on, there on the spot."

—*A. in Quora*

A Hard Dick Is Your Chance To Enjoy The Pleasures Of Submission

I don't mean submission in a degrading or misogynistic sort of way, but in the fullness of pleasure sought. You play with dominance and submission all the time, you've probably just never categorized it in those terms. If you like to be pinned under your guy, you've experienced the thrill of submitting to power. If you like holding him down, you've experienced the thrill of wielding it. It's not possible to have sex without some kind of power exchange. At one moment or another you are wielding or yielding.

In this case, we're talking about yielding to the power of a hard cock. What does that mean? It means losing yourself in the adoration, the ritual of kissing, touching, and suckling on the force, might and power of his hardness. It means giving in to the exhilarating, liberating feeling of being "owned" by his masculinity. Of showing reverence to Strength.

"It's a huge turn on and I can orgasm while doing it. I love pleasuring someone else, taking my time, learning all their little buttons. And the submissive side of me really likes being on my knees."

—*T.*

"Giving blowjobs is a submissive act for me, and I think that's what I love about it. I love being on my knees while my SO [significant other] stands over me, looking up into his eyes for approval, the way he grabs my head by my hair and directs what he wants me to do, how much trouble I get in if I forget the rules and start touching myself during it ... I've absolutely orgasmed while giving a blowjob without even being touched."

—D.

Submission means that by bending your will to the authority vested in his cock you can experience a form of therapeutic escape, of safety, protection. Of glorifying strength and disappearing into the unavoidable nothingness that comes from relinquishing all power. In this scenario, your mouth is a spiritual offering, a way to exalt his command of you.

Damn. Anybody else feel like a biscuit that just got buttered? Whew!

And now more ... butter? Listen to what this straight guy on www.lpsg.com advises on the romance of submission:

"Succumb to his cock ... mentally, physically, emotionally. Give yourself to it. In your mind his cock must be your Sun. It gives you life, you

depend on it. Put it far into your throat, gag slightly on it. Tell him it's overpowering to you. Stroke it with your hands and stare at it like it is made of gold. Think of all the pleasure his cock brings you and reciprocate those feelings. Sit him in a chair, a nice comfy one, and get on your knees in front of him and suck on his cock like he is King of the World. Then tell him to stand up above you, with you on your knees, and ask him to overwhelm you with his cock. Tell him to take control. Obey his cock.

If you can internalize all of this before going into that night, it will show in your performance. I think what really turns a guy on (or at least me) is when you KNOW the girl is truly into it. Truly connected to you and your cock. Totally enamored with it. Techniques and skill pale in comparison to passion and lust."

—T.

A Hard Dick Helps You Experience Submission & Domination Simultaneously

One of the unique things about giving head is that different sexual positions can give you radically different experiences of power. For instance, there's a big difference between giving a blowjob to a man that is lying on his back vs. kneeling in front of him while he stands vs. him sitting relaxed in a chair. The power dynamics just feel different.

Talk to most women who enjoy blowjobs and you'll find that they revel in a hard cock's ability to make them either feel powerful or powerless at almost a moment's notice. As one woman in a discussion forum put it, "the psychological sense of simultaneous submission and power/control is very heady."

"I love giving my man head. I love how in control I feel if he is laying on the bed, or how he can make me feel dirty and submissive if I'm on my knees. Giving my man a 5 star blowy is the fastest way to get me wet and ready for him."

—R.

"I love sucking my partner's cock. It's like the pleasure you get from a good make-out session, plus the turn-on of taking someone inside you, plus the option to switch the dynamic up as you please between submission and control."

—D.

"It makes me feel incredibly sexy. I love the feeling of having all the power while simultaneously feeling the ultimate submission to him."

—W.

A Hard Dick Is The Chance To Take Pleasure From Pleasure Delivered

Pleasure is a coin with two sides. "Heads" means you're giving pleasure and "Tails" means you're getting it. Both states of pleasure exist at the same time. All you have to do is flip the coin to experience one or the other. The pleasure of pleasuring cannot be underestimated or overstated. You know you've achieved a new consciousness about cock when you think, "I would pay HIM for the chance to blow him." Now, that's amore!

"I'm someone who is turned on by my partner being turned on. I love when I can see his toes curl and he grips my hair. I also love hearing him moan. Like... The amount of pleasure I get out of him cursing and telling me how good I am is my favorite thing ever."

—M.

"I love it when they go into overload and start shuddering like they're being hit with little electric shocks and the breathless words they try to form turn into incoherent fragments of linguistic ecstasy—like incantations from the Orgasmanomicon."

—N.

"I love giving blowjobs to my husband! It's so fun and I love to hear how much he loves them. When I have him in my mouth and he's losing

his mind I kinda think 'Wow, I'm making this happen with my freckin mouth' (with a little help from my hands, mostly to support myself and have greater control of his penis). It's pretty awesome! And he returns the favor pretty regularly :)"

—S.

"I really like when guys get vocal. Fucking love it. I enjoy dirty talk but I also just love the sound of a guy moaning, especially if it's almost like a surprise (i.e., as though he wasn't expecting it). I find that giving head is a way to almost guarantee some moaning."

—K.

Again, the pleasure of giving sits side by side with the pleasure of taking. Like Frieda Kahlo's eyebrows, they cannot be separated. Of course, you're not the only one enjoying the scene. Your guy has some, er, skin in the game. But his pleasure isn't always about what you're doing to him. It's as much about what you're making him feel emotionally. Listen to the man who founded www.mydissolutelife.com:

"What do I love about getting blown? So much. Obviously, there are the pleasurable feelings. But they're just the tip of the iceberg. I mean, on the one hand, who wouldn't love sustained,

loving attention to one's cock, to the part of one's body most wired for the receipt of pleasure?

But on the other hand, the bulk of my sexual pleasure and enjoyment happens not in my cock, but in my head: in the land where desire for me is registered. The greatest blowjob, the funnest fuck, pales in comparison to the jolt I receive simply from knowing that you want me – and not just me, but my cock."

A Hard Dick In Your Mouth Can Make You Orgasm

Can blowjobs provide sexual stimulation for women? Yes. Blowjobs have an undeniably big mental component and they can bring women to climax or to the very brink of it.

"Sometimes after a blowjob, my boyfriend runs his finger along my slit and gets a big, dumb smile on his face once he realizes that giving him head actually made me wet."

—S.

"I get physical pleasure from it, definitely. I can feel my pussy muscles clenching while I'm doing it because I get excited and it feels really

nice when they do. But it does feel nice to have a smooth and slippery cock in your mouth and massage it with your lips and tongue. I'm very playful and like to lick and suck all over and get him very slippery. We both get a lot of physical enjoyment out of it LOL."

—T.

"I can and do sometimes orgasm from nothing more than the knowledge that I have my BF's genitals in my mouth. Just thinking about it now makes me all kinds of horny."

—V.

Can You Be A Feminist And Worship Cock?

What a ridiculous question! It's like asking if you can be a feminist and stay at home to take care of the kids. The whole point of feminism (in my humble opinion) is the ability to freely exercise choice without being encumbered by gender expectations. There is a big difference between saying, "I must worship cock because that's my role as a woman" and saying, "I choose to worship cock because it gives me great pleasure."

To me, feminism means owning your sexual desires and expressing them however you see fit.

Raise Your Hand If You DON'T Have An Oral Fixation.

Now, slap yourself with it for being a liar! *Everybody* has an oral fixation to some degree. We've been gleefully putting things in our mouth since we were babies. Why? Because it's pleasurable.

Sure, as we grow older, the oral fixation wanes but it never truly goes away. Almost everybody enjoys the sensation of having something in their mouths. In some, that enjoyment becomes a mild to wild fixation. Whether nail biting or excessive eating, oral fixations are thought to develop during childhood and have a high prevalence among adults.

Oral fixations among women can range from excessive application of lip gloss to the pica disorder, where a woman chews on non-edible materials such as chalk, matches or mattress foam. An overindulgence in any oral fixation could become problematic, but hey, cock tastes a whole lot better than chalk!

So if you've got the slightest proclivity toward an oral fixation (and who doesn't), think of your partner's penis as the thumb you used to suck on when you were a kid (only a lot bigger!). It's comforting. It tastes good. And it feels good.

Just ask him.

"I love dicks and I've always had some degree
of an oral fixation. So blowjobs are like putting

two of my loves together in one activity. When I'm giving a blowjob, I feel like I'm basically checking out a penis up close and personal. It's like eye candy that I can put in my mouth. Every time I stop and start jacking the guy off instead, I'm actually just stopping to visually admire what I'm working with."

—J.

"I ask/beg my partner to do it. It drives me crazy even fantasizing about it. My vulva gets puffy and wet from giving head. Every time. It gives me a similar sensation I get from deep kissing. I think I have an oral fixation."

—G.

Another Great Reason To Give Head: It Brings You Closer

While there are indeed physical pleasures to extract from giving blowjobs, the true treasures are in the psychological highs they unlock. Here, the forbidden nature of oral sex can be re-appropriated for erotic effect, as nothing fuels hedonism like a little naughtiness.

Both you and your man are at your most vulnerable at the onset of oral sex. You may feel emotionally at risk as you prepare to insert his penis into the mouth that you eat, pray and kiss your cat with. Meanwhile, your man is sticking his most sensitive body part into a dark unknown that contains sharp, calcified teeth. This shared vulnerability increases the potential for intimacy by easing each other into comfort, rather than withdrawing into your separate insecurities.

Going down on your guy is one of the best ways to tap into your sexual id and reach heights of arousal that you can't with penetration alone. Sniffing his balls or deeply inhaling his pubic hairs, for example, gives you a big hit of male pheromones, the chemicals that send sexual telegrams to willing recipients. Nothing uncaps your primal desires more than the aroma of rising manhood.

"I do really like giving head! I genuinely enjoy it. But my favorite part of it is when it's over and my boyfriend pulls me up in a big hug and kisses me. He always has the biggest dumbest smile on his face and he is so cute and tired and it makes me happy to know that I can make him feel good."

—J.

What If You Don't Like Giving Head?

A husband and wife went to see a marriage counselor because they were unhappy about their sex lives. The therapist, in an attempt to find some common ground, said, "Tell me anything the two of you have in common."

The husband said, "Well, neither one of us sucks dicks."

A lot of women look at penises and think of Mink Stole's immortal words in the John Waters film, Female Trouble: *"I wouldn't suck your lousy dick if I was suffocating and there was oxygen in your balls."*

Please, God, I hope you're not one of them. But if you are, no worries, because this next section is going to help you overcome your aversion to giving head.

So Why Do You Hate It? It's important to understand that you inherited much of your dislike from the messages society has been sending women for eons—that giving head signals submissiveness (and not the good kind), lower status and humiliation.

When a guy yells, "Suck my dick!" outside of the bedroom (and sometimes in it) he means it as an insult. It's designed to show power, to degrade. There's a certain arrogance in guys expecting you to get on your knees and service them. Porn takes this degradation to the extreme, showing men "punishing" women with their cocks and climaxing on their faces in the most humiliating way possible. So it isn't crazy, given these cultural facts, for some women to be uneasy with the power dynamics that are associated with oral sex. They may be overcome by shame or view a blowjob at the very least as a non-reciprocal sexual act, where they do all the work and men get all the pleasure.

Slut Shaming and Such

Many women believe that it's not ladylike to give a blowjob, and that even their boyfriends or husbands will view them as trashy the moment their lips touch their cocks. No woman wants to be seen as easy (I prefer "agreeable"—it's so less judgmental!).

This insecurity, of course, governs much of female sexuality beyond blowjobs, as we are taught to believe that a woman's worth is tied to her sexual purity, and that her sexual organs exist solely for the purpose of producing babies. But women are not numb, reproductive factories. You are fully developed human beings, with the ability to both give and receive sexual pleasure, and you should not be shamed for making use of those abilities.

Today, the meaning of oral sex has dramatically changed for the better. While some of the negative vestiges remain, far more powerful ones have taken root. In recent surveys, more than three-quarters of all American women have given a man a blowjob, and polls suggest that folks are engaging in more oral sex with greater casualness. Men, realizing their language about blowjobs discourage women from doing something they desperately want them to do, have changed their tone markedly in the last couple of decades. They've gone from disparaging it to begging for it.

So now that you're not fighting against a culture that defined it as punishment or a history that considered it slutty, you're free to make blowjobs mean whatever you want. Of course, the first order of business is to actually *like* doing it.

If you've tried and didn't like it there are a few things that can change it around. But wait, you might be thinking...

If You Don't Like It, Why Should You Have To Change?

You don't. But how many times in your life have you tried something that you initially didn't like and ended up loving? No one likes their first martini, for example. But then the buzz works its magic and next thing you know you're drinking so many that olives come out every time you pee.

Which reminds me, why is alcoholism the only disease you get yelled at for having?

At any rate, if you find yourself a little resistant to blowjobs, think about all the times you didn't like something in the beginning and came to love at the end. The television show that was uninteresting the first couple of episodes, for example, that turned into must-see TV. Or the Pulitzer prize-winning book that bored you in the first couple of chapters and then turned into all-night page-turner.

Have you ever noticed that some things feel a lot better with more practice? Dancing, learning a language or cooking, for example. There's not that much enjoyment to be had in the beginning. At first, you're stressed and self-conscious and uncertain of the best way to proceed. But with practice and experience you get a lot more enjoyment out of them. Blowjobs are like that. Once you understand what works for you and what doesn't, once you understand strategies to help you enjoy it more and get better at it, chances are you'll completely change your mind. Whether you're in the kitchen, the ballroom, a classroom or your bedroom, practice doesn't just make perfect, it makes pleasure.

Millions of women have changed their minds about blowjobs but only after they got clear about what they needed to make it enjoyable. I am particularly taken by this woman's experience:

"When it comes to blowjobs, I've traveled the full spectrum from hate to love and it really depends on the partner. I've never loved sucking a man's cock as much as I love my current fwb [friend with benefits]. Things that really help:

- *I find his penis excruciatingly gorgeous.*

- *Great hygiene—hair is well-kept, always smells clean, doesn't put any cologne down there (tastes horrible).*

- *He experiments with dominant/porny moves but always **always** immediately stops if I say or imply a no. He's really amazing about that. He'll go from brutally fucking my throat to gentle and caring if I push him away or shake my head. I really don't mind pigtail-grabbing, head-pushing, etc.,* *but the #1 thing is that I have to know in my heart that if I ever feel like it's too much he WILL stop. I've had guys in the past who made me uneasy, like maybe they weren't just role-playing, you know?*

- *Appreciative noises. So important. My last ex was so quiet and it made it hard to feel encouraged and I had no idea how close he was. My current guy moans and says little things to cue me into how he's doing.*

- *Nice-shaped balls to suck on. Balls are fun."*

You Shouldn't Be Doing It For Him.

The first thing that'll help you change your mind about blowjobs is to reframe why you're doing it. Whenever we do something *for* somebody else we quickly turn it into a "chore." A job. An unwelcome necessity to keep your partner happy. Here's a perfect example of how resentful some women feel about giving oral:

"I work just as many hours as him. I do all of the cleaning and most of the cooking. I handle the bills and appointments and make arrangements and do the errands. What does he do? He comes home, sometimes goes to the gym

and then sits on the computer all night talking to people via Facebook or he goes out to the garage to work on his motorcycle.

Where's my worshiping? I just don't think I should have to pay him extra special attention just to get something in return out of my relationship with him. Right now, I think things are pretty even in ours. We love each other. Spend a decent amount of time together, etc."

—*C. from www.aphroditewomenshealth.com*

Obviously, this couple has more issues than *Vogue Magazine*, but it does point to a classic perception that many women have about oral sex—as something you do in return for something else, like good behavior. If you're going to exact revenge for whatever he's doing wrong in the relationship then for God sake's, punish HIM not yourself. Cut the cable during a football game, not your access to his crotch.

Many women also see giving head as an unpleasant but necessary way to gain leverage over a man. It's the classic "sexual favor" that results in a non-sexual reward, as illustrated by this 1950s-style joke:

A little boy comes home from school and announces that he learned where babies come from. Amused, the mother asks him to explain.

"The mommy and daddy take off all of their clothes. Then, the daddy's noodle stands up and mommy puts it in her mouth. It explodes in her mouth and that's where babies come from."

The mom shakes her head in sadness and corrects him. "Oh, honey," she says. "That's not where babies come from. That's where *jewelry* comes from."

That's a joke with an ugly premise: Blowjobs are a means to an end rather than a pleasure to be enjoyed. If this is your view, I invite you to re-read the first half of this chapter and get in touch with how sexually satisfying blowjobs can be FOR YOU.

That said, there's actually nothing wrong with being so good at head that it results in jewelry! There's also nothing wrong with using sex to get your way outside of the bedroom. When I was a kid I had a lemonade stand. I gave the first glass away for free but charged five dollars for the second. The refill contained the antidote. My point, and I do have one, is a) Don't ever drink anything I hand you, and b) It's okay to leverage your assets for personal gain.

Blowjobs As A Special Treat

The idea that blowjobs should be reserved for something special is yet another attitude from a bygone era that still finds purchase today. You've heard it before (and some of you have actually said something like it): "It's Valentine's Day, I'm going to surprise him with a blowjob."

It's like the story of the old man and the cookie. He was lying on his death bed. With only hours to live, he suddenly notices the scent of chocolate chip cookies coming from the kitchen. With his last bit of energy, the old man pulls himself out of his bed, across the floor to the stairs, and down the stairs to the kitchen. There, the old man's wife was baking chocolate chip cookies. With his last ounce of energy, the old man reaches for a cookie.

His wife smacks him across the back of his hand, and hisses, *"Leave them alone, they're for your funeral!"*

My point, and I do have one, is that you shouldn't "save the blowjobs" for something special. If you find yourself thinking like that, STOP. You're still operating under the anti-quated belief that blowjobs are for his pleasure alone and not yours. Besides, how good can your blowjobs be if you only do them on special days? *Practice* is what separates *Meh* from MEOW!

Are You Groaning About Groins?

Perhaps the reason you don't enjoy giving blowjobs is because you think penises are icky. Or maybe the guys you've gone down on smelled like swamp ass.

There's also understandable anxiety about one's mouth coming in contact with the part of a man's body that excretes bodily waste. Even if not a drop of his pee enters your mouth, plenty of women can't tolerate the faint scent of urine and sweat that can build up while his package is tucked into underwear.

Unlike ovens, a man's penis is not self-cleaning, so it's important to make sure your partner washes his private areas thoroughly before oral sex. This is especially important for uncut guys, as their foreskin retains a natural lubricant known as smegma, which can accumulate and acquire an unappealing odor.

If you've had bad experiences with smells and odors, good news! Your man can cure it with soap and water! Yes, it's that easy. Sometimes you've got to draw a line in the sand by punishing bad behavior ("no bjs for you, buddy, until you clean up!") and rewarding good, clean deeds ("Spread your legs, I'm coming in!"). The simple truth is that you have to be demanding of your men. Quick story to make my point:

A Jewish grandma and her grandson are at the beach. He's playing in the water, she is standing on the shore, not wanting to get her feet wet, when all of a sudden, a huge wave appears from nowhere and crashes directly onto the spot where the boy is wading. The water recedes and the boy is no longer there. He was swept away.

The grandma holds her hands to the sky, screams and cries: "Lord, how could you? Haven't I been a wonderful grandmother? Haven't I been a wonderful mother? Haven't I kept a kosher home? Haven't I given to the B'nai B'rith? Haven't I lit candles every Friday night? Haven't I tried my very best to live a life that you would be proud of?"

A voice booms from the sky, "All right already!"

A few minutes later another huge wave appears out of nowhere and crashes on the beach. As the water recedes, the boy is standing there. He is smiling and splashing around as if nothing had ever happened.

The voice booms again. "I have returned your grandson. Are you satisfied?"

She responds, "He had a hat."

My point, and I do have one, is that you must demand more of your men if they expect a blowjob. Take heart from these demanding women, who make no bones about their expectations:

"I only, ONLY give blowjobs if the guy looks after himself, especially down there (shaven, cleaned, and a good diet). I've dated guys who didn't look after themselves (bad diet, didn't think about cleaning down there, didn't shave) and it's unpleasant to the point where the cum made me want to hurl.

I've also given blowjobs to guys who did look after themselves. One guy in particular was very into being in tip-top condition, had a Pinterest-worthy diet and he was a bit of a clean freak. It was absolutely magical to suck his dick. It was smooth and everything smelled nice. His cum had the slightest sweet tinge to the taste but other than that it was tasteless and had no smell, and it was so smooth and silky in my mouth too. I literally could have sucked his dick all day. He was also very vocal about his pleasure, which I found satisfying. I think there is a lot to be said for having a guy look after himself down there."

—N.

"I love blowjobs only if guys meet my criteria. If it's a dick that I really find attractive, attached to a guy who knows what he's doing

in that department (grooming, diet for the sake of cum taste, etc.), I want to suck it for hours. Even longer if it's a guy who's vocal and shows the pleasure he's receiving through squirms and moans and shudders."

—A.

"I can't feel like I'm OBLIGATED to blow him. When I go down on my manfriend, I really want to, and I suck that thing like I'm on The Price is Right and I want to win the fucking convertible. You've got to worship the dick, but on YOUR terms. That's all I'm sayin'."

—D.

"I won't give blowjobs to casual or non serious partners because I view it as more intimate than PIV [penis in vagina] sex. And if my partner doesn't make any noises of appre-ciation I don't like giving them either."

—B.

But It's Uncomfortable!

Some women actually like giving head but don't want to put up with the physical discomfort they experience. Their lips are easily stretched to the limits of their elasticity, or they can't take more than two inches before they choke like a crow with too much in its craw.

We'll explore overcoming the physical discomfort of giving head in the next chapter, so you can cross discomfort off your list now. Meantime, admit it, do you...

Suck at Sucking?

If the reason you don't enjoy giving oral sex is because you're bad at it, I admire your self-awareness. Maybe you've been told your blowjobs are heartless, dry and toothy, and you see no point in subjecting other penises to such mistreatment. Bartender, another round of lack of confidence, please!

Kudos to your sensitivity, but incompetence is a flimsy excuse to rob yourself of giving or receiving pleasure. I remember a girlfriend telling me that after one of her first attempts at giving a blowjob, her date said, "If this were a restaurant, I'd send it back." She was crushed. But not for long, because it gave her the determination to get better.

Like anything, practice is the best way to perfect blowjobs, but my guess is that unlike my girlfriend, you don't want to practice BJs on a daily basis. If you do, more power to you, but there is an alternate way to learn the art of oral seduction: Watch blow porn.

Studies show that watching erotic films increases genital blood flow in women. No surprise there. But you might be shocked to find porn doesn't elevate testosterone levels, which are crucial to your libido.

Wait, how can that be? Turns out that the majority of bompchicka-wow-wow porn is physiologically but not psycho-logically arousing for women. You may get physically excited because you're witnessing skin-to-skin contact, but it's doubtful you'll get psychologically or emotionally aroused. Why? Because those videos lack what is psychologically stimulating for women—intimacy, attractive men, appealing sex acts, sexual tension, interesting dialogue, realistically-shaped women, foreplay, kissing, the list goes on.

So how do you pick the kind of porn that is both physiologically and psychologically arousing? Once, a rather conservative, religious friend of mine checked into a hotel and asked if the porn channel in his room was disabled. The clerk said, *"No, it's regular porn, you sick bastard."*

You will love to give head—and do it well—if you see it as a principal way for you to pleasure yourself, not just him

Now, you might be like my friend and find all porn offensive, or you could be like the clerk and only find certain types that are out of bounds. Either way, research on female sexual response is clear: Women get more sexually excited when they see erotic films that are specifically made for women. They have everything that'll turn you on: Credible actors, emotion-infused sex, attentive men, authentic stories, genuine chemistry, interesting locations, and yes, real women's orgasms.

They also feature something you rarely see in men's porn: Women with a wide variety of shapes and sizes.

To find the most current women-centered porn head to www.goodforher.com, which produces an annual "feminist porn awards show." For a comprehensive list of women-centered erotica, visit www.pornmoviesforwomen.com. In the meantime, here's a women-curated list of must-see classics:

1. Afrodite Superstar
2. Trial Run
3. Pirates
4. Uniform Behavior
5. Insatiable
6. Fashion Underground
7. Edge Play
8. Chemistry
9. Night Trips
10. Paid Companions

In an ancient monastery in a faraway place, a new monk arrived to join his brothers in copying books and scrolls in the monastery's scriptorium. He was assigned as a scriptor on copies of books that had already been copied by hand.

One day he asked Father Florian (the Armarius of the Scriptorium), "Does not the copying by hand of other copies allow for chances of error? How do we know we are not copying the mistakes of someone else? Are they ever checked against the original?"

Fr. Florian is set back a bit by the obvious logical observation of this youthful monk. "A very good point, my son. I will take one of the latest books down to the vault and compare it against the original."

Fr. Florian went down to the secured vault and began his verification. After a day had passed, the monks began to worry and went down looking for the old priest. They were sure something must have happened. As they approached the vault, they heard sobbing and crying. When they opened the door, they found Fr. Florian sobbing over the new copy on the table. It was obvious to all that the poor man had been crying his heart out for a long time.

"What is the problem, Reverend Father?" asked one of the monks. "Oh, my Lord," sobbed the priest, "The word is *celebrate!*"

The point to this story, and there really is one, is that you should not take a vow of oral celibacy. Celebrate! The party is in your mouth!

Let's Review.

Why would you want to show some oral love to masculinity's Main Representative? For starters, a hard dick is the very symbol of masculinity—something you crave and appreciate in a man.

A rock hard cock is also proof that you're beautiful and desirable. There should be no greater compliment to you than having your partner's erect cock pointing straight at you. It is proof of your desirability. In that regard, the penis could be seen quite rightly as being all about *you*. So when you go down on him, you're not doing him a favor. You're giving yourself a gift.

Oral sex also gives you the opportunity to feel contradictory yet simultaneous feelings of dominance and submission. And who doesn't like that?!

Free Your Mind, Your Mouth Will Follow

Remember, blowjobs aren't tasks; they're turn-ons. Think about why you love his penis, not just what you can do with it or to it. Is it the thrill of feeling him get hard in your mouth? The power to arouse him? The feeling of submission when you look up at his eyes? Its strength and hardness? Its masculine smell and feel? How it can dominate you? Is it the sheer novelty of seeing and feeling a part of him you don't ordinarily see? The anticipation of bathing it with your mouth before it's inserted into your body?

"I get so incredibly turned on when I give my man head. I like to strip down and get on my knees and then blow him so he can watch and can control the movement by placing his hands on the back of my head. I will blow him every chance I get. Sometimes he has to push

me away. I love the feel, the taste, the sensa-
tion. Any woman who doesn't like this activity
is insane."

—Y.

Without thinking about, acting on, and expressing your love for his dick, you're just going through the motions. Remember talent without passion makes you a skilled laborer, not a worthy lover. Get in touch with why giving oral is pleasurable for *you*, and you'll be able to combine skill with passion to create a memorable experience. When it comes to sex, it's better to suck at something you love than to excel at something you don't.

Now that you've gotten in touch with why you pant for penis, you're ready to learn some techniques, so let's get started. By the time I'm done, your blowjobs are going to hit your partner harder than the bottom of a whiskey bottle at an Irish wake. And they're going to do for your satisfaction what a vibrator does for your orgasms.

Let Cocktoberfest begin!

Chapter Two

Know How It Works Before You Work It

How well do you know a man's sexual plumbing? Now, I can already hear you saying, "But Sister Stepanowitz already taught me about male anatomy in junior high sex ed!" Let's pause and think about that for a second: it's very likely that your knowledge of male sexual satisfaction came from an underpaid, sexually frustrated virgin while you were perfecting your zit-popping technique.

Most women overestimate their knowledge of male sexual anatomy just like men overestimate their knowledge of yours. If you want to give Category 5 Blowjobs you're going to need to know a lot more about the one-eyed trouser trout. The only way to work it right is to know how it works in the first place. So, let's get started and make Sister Stepanowitz proud!

You Have A Penis, Too, You Know!
When actress Tallulah Bankhead was asked if 1950s heart-throb Tab Hunter was gay she replied, *"I don't know, darling, he's never sucked my cock."* She was actually onto something. The most astounding thing about men and

women is that despite how differently we look, our bodies are mirror images of each other. Males and females start out as identical blobs of tissue when the sperm enters the egg. Even with ultrasound, you can't tell the difference between male and female babies until the 15th week of pregnancy.

The same tissue that turns into ovaries in women turns into testicles for men. The same tissue that forms vaginal lips in women forms scrotal sacs in men. The same tissue that turns into a penis in men turns into a clitoris for women. In fact, both the penis and clitoris have a glans and a shaft and become engorged with blood when sexually stimulated. So much for penis envy.

So What Exactly Happens When He Gets Hard?

There are four stages of sexual arousal. Well, five, but we're not counting the part where he rolls over, falls asleep and snores. Let's take a look at each stage:

Arousal: How A Dangling Taco Turns Into A Raging Burrito.

For men, sex starts with seeing, thinking, touching, smelling or fantasizing about something or someone that turns them on. Like a gorgeous woman or a new BMW. Whatever. Extra blood starts pumping to key areas of the body—the penis, scrotum, genitals, lips, earlobes and other parts. Men get an erection when the two large cylinders of spongy tissue in their penis fill with blood. A tough fibrous sheath covers these cylinders. When those cylinders fill up with blood they push against this sheath much the way pumping air into a tire pushes against the rubber walls. This creates something strong enough to take a ride on. The muscles in the scrotum contract, moving the testicles upwards toward the pelvis.

Plateau: "Faster! Harder! Don't Stop!"

In this stage, everything swells, lifts and darkens. Pleasure fluctuates with highs and lows but never ends. It's perfectly natural for erections to wax and wane in the plateau stage. For instance, he may lose his erection while going down on you even though he loves doing it. No worries. All it means is that giving oral sex doesn't keep him hard. He'll get it back. The plateau stage is where most of the manual, oral and penetrative sex happens. Most people want to establish residency here because it just feels too good to leave.

Orgasm: Spectacula like Dracula!

As men advance from the plateau stage the pleasure peaks and they start gasping toward "ejaculatory inevitability" (the point where nothing is going to stop the orgasm—not even his mom walking in on him). Here's what happens: Everything starts to contract. His testicles ascend until they press against the wall of the pelvis. The prostate, seminal vesicles and vas deferens squeeze themselves silly, pouring their sperm and seminal fluid like bartenders who can't keep up with the orders. The head of the penis becomes deep purple while the shaft increasingly stiffens. Breathing, blood pressure and heartbeat increase as the total-body response to ejaculation takes over. Involuntary spasms in the legs, feet, toes, stomach, arms and back can take over. The pelvic muscles go through a series of rhythmic contractions, ejaculating semen through the urethra as a series of spurts.

And that, in a nutshell, is how every other thought men have during the day ends at night.

Resolution: The Fancy Word For Rolling Over And Snoring.

You know how everything contracts during orgasm? The opposite happens during the resolution phase. It's as if your body got shot to the moon and now it's gravity's turn to teach you a lesson. The blood flows out of the penis and the scrotum descends. Pulse, breathing and blood pressure rates return to normal. After climaxing, women can have another go at sex right away. Men can't, because they go through a refractory period in which they can't get erect. For some it's a minute or two; for others a day or two. For most, somewhere in between, depending on age and circumstances. At any rate, the tension released by orgasm feels exquisite to men. That's why the first syllable in orgasm should be spelled "ohhh."

Now, united you may have stood (or laid), but divided you shall fall: Women tend to be more alert after orgasm while men become somewhat catatonic. That's because different things happen in their bodies. Oxytocin, the "cuddle chemical," tends to flood women after sex, while men get drained of glycogen, a vital source for energy. And that's why women want to bond after sex and men want to snore.

Let's Talk About Dick

I have a friend who calls his penis "Richard" because it's long for Dick. I bring this up for two reasons. One, guys will often give their penises a pet name. Two, the nickname will always insinuate that his dick is so big it's in the next room mixing drinks.

Be that as it may, the penis can sometimes get a bad rap. We call rude, aggressive guys "pricks" and characterize cruel actions as "dick moves." Clearly, the penis needs a little PR.

It's all too common to oversimplify the penis as a dumb burrito, just hanging around with his two bros all day until it's time to urinate or ejaculate. In reality, the cock is a nuanced, complicated, beautiful creation that ought to be understood and appreciated in full, not sucked or stroked mindlessly. It's strong but sensitive, hard but fleshy and the external expression of a man's soul. Granted, the vagina is rightly revered as a sacred part of humanity and the source of life, but the penis is essential in the equation of humankind, too. We're going to show it a little respect by learning about its quirks and hidden desires. Let's take a closer look:

Fans of The Glans

If you put a tuxedo on a guy's penis, the glans is the part that would be above the bow tie. The head might be considered the public face of the penis, its spokesman. If the penis has got anything to say, it's the head that will do the talking (be careful though, because it's known to spit when it speaks). It's the mushroom-shaped tip of the penis that is visible on guys who have been circumcised, and which magically appears when the foreskin is pulled back on uncut guys. Peekaboo!

The penis glans has a much higher concentration of nerve endings than the shaft, so the head is an essential part of bringing a man satisfaction and release. The glans has a coronal ridge separating it from the shaft (the outer edge of the "helmet"). Sexual scientists have identified the head as being the most significant area of stimulation the closer a guy is to climaxing, and you can only imagine the experiments that were used to reach that obvious conclusion.

The glans likes to be licked, kissed, sucked and rubbed against the insides of your mouth and throat. It should never come in contact with your teeth for the same reason Kanye West should never come in contact with a microphone: Someone's going to get hurt. The head of a penis is very sensitive—baring your teeth will do it no favors.

The head of the penis is more diverse and complex than it appears at first *glans*, so let's get on our knees and take a closer look at what we're about to put in our mouths.

The Eye Of The Tiger: His Peehole

Ever notice that the penis always seems to have a mischievous grin? That's the urinary meatus, commonly known as the pee hole—the opening through which urine and cum flow. There are two lips covering the pee hole and they're dying for a kiss. Pucker up!

Although what comes out of the pee hole may gross you out, know that there are relatively few "germs" in urine due to the ammonia it contains. If a man washes properly his dick is generally one of the cleanest parts of his body.

You can dramatically increase the pleasure you get out of giving blowjobs if you concentrate on what attracts you to his penis.

But the urinary meatus is more than just a utilitarian tube for bodily fluids. It is a supremely sensitive part of the custard cannon and can be tenderly stimulated with licking and kissing. In fact, here's a little known secret: "French kissing" the pee hole will catapult you into the blowjob hall of fame contention. The sensation is so delicious, so unbelievably stimulating that the laziest guy on earth will turn to you and say, *"You make me want to get a job."*

Why Is The Head Of The Penis Shaped Like A Mushroom?

One theory is that it is designed to be more like a shovel, or specifically a "semen displacement device." Scientists at the State University of New York at Albany speculate that the penis evolved into a shape that allowed the second or third guy entering a woman's vagina to "scoop out" the semen of the men who ejaculated inside her prior to his own entrance.

"Thus, the human penis may enable males to substitute their semen for the semen of their competitors," the researchers wrote.

The V-Spot: His Frenulum

Did you know that dicks have a V-spot – a sort of hot spot in an already erotic zone? It's a small triangular region where a thin strip of skin called the frenulum attaches to the glans. The frenulum is the band of tissue that connects the foreskin on the underside of a man's penis to the corona; on circumcised guys, the frenulum streams toward the corona in a V shape, which is how this pleasure zone derived its nickname.

The V-spot is loaded with erogenous nerves that can amplify a man's orgasm. If it's true that men think with their penis, then this is the command center. The V-spot responds to caressing, whether with your tongue, lips or fingers. Those who master the art of pleasing it will be rewarded with a penis that acts like a puppy at mealtime.

Get Shafted

Ahhhh, it's time to meet Big Daddy. The shaft is what separates a two-inch cock from a ten-inch monster. It defines a guy's sense of manhood (which is why so many guys lie about its length), and makes your mouth water when you imagine it sliding into your mouth.

The shaft is the part of the penis that runs from the base of the head to a guy's balls, and it comes in an infinite variety of lengths, girths, curves and textures. Sometimes it's smooth and sometimes it's veiny, sometimes it's short and thick and sometimes it's long and lanky. Sometimes the oral sex stars align and it's long, thick and worthy of the name "Richard."

The shaft is filled with erectile tissue that expands and contracts based on a guy's arousal and blood flow. Compared to the uniform sensitivity of the head, the shaft is more versatile when it comes to the amount of pressure or friction applied.

The Boys In The Band: Balls

What do you have when you're holding two balls in your hand? A man's full attention. What's known commonly as a man's balls, or nuts, or marbles, or twins is the duo composed of the testicles and scrotum. The testicles are the "family jewels" themselves, and the scrotum is the antique silk sack that stores the jewels. Together, they are the origin of life—literally where it all begins. The balls are where semen is produced, making them essential to the reproductive process.

Considering their stature as the source from which all of humanity flows, the balls often don't receive nearly the appreciation they deserve when it comes to being stimulated.

Fondling a man's balls should be included in your blowjob starter-pack, as it's a sign of competency and to my mind, *decency*. Remaining mindful that the testicles are extremely sensitive, they can be stimulated by touching, tugging, licking and humming. Yes, humming. Place his balls in your mouth, hum "Ommm," and learn why Buddhists consider that sound to be the highest expression of consciousness.

A No Man's Land Called The Perineum

I was talking with a few friends recently and one of them said that a blowjob simply consists of sucking the penis and fondling the balls.

"Taint!" I protested.

The perineum, more commonly known as the "taint" (cuz it t'aint the balls and it t'aint the ass), resembles buried gold: hidden from sight, and filled with riches. The strip of tissue is concentrated with nerve endings, making it an obvious candidate to be licked and sucked. The taint is also an outer access point for what's widely considered a man's inner G-spot, the prostate.

Playing with the taint can boost a guy's pleasure receptors more than an open bar at a strip club. It also opens the door to new regions of arousal, specifically the back door. Speaking of which, let's talk about...

Butthole Surfers: His Rectum

Our tour of the hidden world of male pleasure now takes us to the butt hole, or more formally, the rectum. While it might seem like a foreign land, a guy's butt hole plays an important role during sex, especially when he climaxes. The rectum contracts in rhythm with the genitals during orgasm, meaning the butt hole is so rich with nerves that it propels a guy's climax with him likely being unaware of it. Imagine what awaits when a little extra attention is paid to it!

The butt hole contains two rings known as sphincters, which work independently and in different fashions. Men have control over the external sphincter as they can flex and contract it. The internal sphincter is controlled by an involuntary part of the nervous system so it's harder to control consciously. Fortunately, both sphincters can be trained and tamed to allow sensuous finger play. More on that later.

The Male WTF Spot! His Prostate

While western religions have helped turn the male anus into a forbidden zone in the bedroom, other belief systems have assigned mystical importance to what's hiding in a guy's butt. The Tantra philosophy, which has influenced Buddhism and Hinduism, considers the prostate a sacred spot and a man's emotional center. Does that mean if he's being a pain in the ass he's just trying to understand himself better? Doubtful, but isn't it rich to think that the way to his soul might be through his butt hole?

The prostate gland is a walnut-shaped bulb located about 2-3 inches inside a guy's rectum. The fluid excreted by the prostate makes up about one-third of the total volume of semen and contains various enzymes, zinc and citric acid. You can "milk" the prostate by sliding your finger into a guy's anus, then tickling or stroking the prostate in a down-ward motion.

Now that you know how a penis is built and how it works, let's take a look at some sexy examples. Get ready for our pictorial list, *The 20 Most Beautiful Erect Penises In The World*. If dicks are real estate, you're about to take a tour of ocean front property.

Chapter Three

The 20 Most Beautiful
Erect Penises In The World

What makes a beautiful cock? It's a question for the ages—and a science lab, it turns out. Scientists at the University of Zurich recently published a study in The Journal of Sexual Medicine that asked just that question.

They showed a focus group of over 100 women ages 16-45 a wide range of erect penises (nice work if you can get it!) and asked them to rank the importance of eight penile characteristics ranging from length to pubic hair.

What characteristic came in at #1? Most men would predict SIZE, but they'd be wrong. Actually, they'd be wrong on stilts. In order of importance, this is how women ranked penile characteristics:

1. General cosmetic appearance

2. Appearance of pubic hair

3. Penile skin

4. Penile girth

5. Shape of glans

6. Penile length

7. Appearance of scrotum

8. Position and shape of meatus (urethra)

There are a couple of things worth nothing about these results. First, women care more about the overall appearance of a penis rather than any one characteristic.

Second, size didn't even make the top three preferences. And when it did make an appearance at #4 it was an aspect of size that men rarely focus on—girth. A girlfriend perfectly captured this preference over our second, okay, third bottle of wine. "It's not the length I like in a penis," she said. "It's the roundth!"

The definition of a beautiful cock is simple: It's something that hangs off a guy you find beautiful.

The "appearance of pubic hair" placed a surprisingly strong second and this provides us with an opportunity to significantly increase your attraction to his penis: Manscaping. We'll talk more about getting him to trim his pubic hair in the next chapter, but for now I want to emphasize why it's so important to increase your attraction to his penis. It's simple: The more you pant for it, the more turned on you'll be when you're blowing him. Remember, this book is not just about better techniques to use on him but about increasing the pleasure you get out of applying them.

Okay, let's get back to the definition of a beautiful penis.

Academic studies may reveal preferences in penile characteristics but the question of beauty remains in the eyes of
the cock holder. Here's one woman's articulate paean to a
pretty penis:

*I've told my boyfriend that he has the cock
that all dildos wish they could be, and it's oh so
true. And it IS just beautiful. I think good
proportions are the most important part. It
has the perfect girth for his length, and the
head matches the shaft just right. And I like a
little bit of vein popping up here and there. He
has this amazing, thick vein right on top. And
his balls seem to fit the whole package perfectly.
He's circumcised and keeps his hair trimmed,
but not shaved bare, which matches my preferences perfectly.*

*I could go on for days about his cock. I want to
make a mold of it and send it to a museum. I
actually googled "perfect cock" to see if I could
find a picture for comparison, but I like his
better than all those examples. Simply put,
when you see a beautiful cock, you know it."*

—B.

Personally, I think the definition of a beautiful cock is
simple: It hangs off a guy you find beautiful. You can talk all

you want about symmetry, girth, or a well-manicured bed of pubes, a stellar dick on a gross guy means nothing. The guy attached to it matters the most.

One description I found particularly illuminating came from a straight guy (of all people!):

I'm not a lady ... or even a gay dude ... but ... I think straight women find cocks 'beautiful' in the same way straight men find vaginas (vulvas) beautiful.

Is a vulva really beautiful?? Really?? Probably not. But straight men are 'hard wired' to find it so. A straight man finds a vulva 'beautiful' not just because of that it looks like but also because of what it feels like, smells like, tastes like, and because of the emotions (intimacy) he feels when he makes love to someone he cares about. It's for ALL of these reasons that a straight man will consider a vulva 'beautiful'. Not JUST because of how it looks.

I assume it is the same for cocks. Is a cock 'beautiful' in it's own right?? I have no doubt some women might say yes. But she might also find it beautiful for other reasons like how it makes her feel physically and emotionally... because it belongs to someone she loves.

Just thank God or Mother Nature that men and women find each other attractive... and in ways much more complex than mere 'beauty'."
                                                                —G.

I think he's right. When women say a cock is 'beautiful' they are referring to both its appearance AND the pleasure it gives them. A metaphor may be found in something else you put in your mouth—food. You may say that a meal was beautiful, but you would never limit the definition to how it looked on the plate. You'd also describe how good it tasted and how satisfied it made you feel.

Okay, enough with theories on pretty pee pees. I invite you to look at what my editorial team (six women) considers *The 20 Most Beautiful Erect Penises In World.* We scoured thousands of websites, picked the top 100 pictures and put them to a vote.

While we would have loved to publish the images here in the book, the logistics of identifying photographers, getting their contact information, agreeing on a licensing cost, and making the payments were practically impossible for one simple reason: Most of the images we found on the internet did not identify the photographer. As it is a copyright violation to publish pictures without the consent of the photographer, we opted not to publish them here but to post them online.

So paste the link below in your browser, pour yourself a stiff one and get ready to say "OMG" in twenty different ways.

The 20 Most Beautiful Erect Penises In The World.
LINK: callmemaybe.us/pics

Chapter Four

A Simple Technique To Make His Penis More Attractive To You

Can a man change the appearance of his penis to make it more desirable to you? Yes, according to the University of Zürich study you read about in the last chapter. The study showed that the appearance of pubic hair was the second most important penile characteristic to women. Well, guess what? That's a trait men have the power to change. The single best thing your partner can do to make his penis more attractive to you is to trim and style his pubic hair. And it's a change you should absolutely request he make. After all, this is about *your* pleasure. The more turned on you can get by his penis the more satisfying a blowjob will be for both of you.

The Cucumber Looks Best When It Rises Out Of A Salad.

An overgrown garden can easily hide a beautiful cucumber. Landscape it and suddenly you can see the vegetable in all its glory. Besides, a dense bush can make going down on a guy problematic. You could, for example, get stray pubic hairs in your mouth. Not a good look. Or smell. A lot of hair traps moisture providing a breeding ground for odor-causing bacteria. Get it landscaped and poof! No stray pubic hairs, no funny smells.

Are there benefits for him? Absolutely. First, it creates what I call an "optical inch." Some guys are so hairy down there that their dicks look small. Manicure their pelvic lawns and bam! They look an inch bigger. So if you think he's going to resist trimming his bush tell him his penis will look a lot bigger and I promise he'll knock over your grandmother trying to get to the scissors.

There are other benefits for him, too. Believe it or not, it'll improve his sex life. Hair tends to block subtle sensations on the skin. There you are devoting love and attention with a warm, wet mouth and he's only feeling half of it because his pubes are cock-blocking your caresses!

The single best thing your partner can do to make his penis more attractive to you is to trim his pubic hair.

Scream-Free Manscaping

He's got to be extra careful trimming back his pubic hair or his dick will look like it went on a date with "Carrie." Once, my boyfriend got ingrown hairs and cut himself so badly I took one look at the blood in the bathroom and I called the suicide hotline. He was like, "Dude, if I was going to kill myself I'd cut my wrist, not my balls!"

Because your partner would be shaving such sensitive areas it's a good idea to tell him this story:

The Army was offering veteran soldiers early retirement after the first Gulf War. The rule: Soldiers picked two spots on their bodies and got $1,000 for every inch in between.

One officer asked to be measured from the top of his head to the tip of his toes. He was 6 feet tall and got $72,000.

A second, smarter officer asked to be measured from the tip of his raised hand to his toes. He earned $96,000.

The third man was a grizzled old captain. "Measure me from the tip of my penis to my testicles," he demanded. The medical officer in charge explained that might not be terribly profitable. But the captain insisted. He dropped his pants; the MD placed the tape measure on the tip of the captain's penis and began to work back.

"My God!" the MD gasped. "Where are your testicles?" The captain yells, "Iraq!"

Moral of the story: Your partner needs to be careful trimming his pubes or his balls will end up where they don't belong—like your bathtub. Now, here's a stellar idea: Instead of getting him to landscape his own Versailles, why not turn it into sex play? As you know, "Getting your hair did" at the salon is a sensuous experience. Imagine the same feelings experienced below the belt. One of the most sensuous moments of my life was letting a partner wash, trim and style my pubic hair. It created an unexpected sense of trust and intimacy. Given the potential of an ugly outcome I HAD to trust him, stand still and hope to hell he didn't turn into Edward Scissorhands. He honored that trust, too, with an incredible attention to detail. It actually bonded us in a way that made future sex even hotter.

While it may be work for you to do the trimming, the upside is that you get to shape it to *your* liking not his. Which again, is an important aspect to getting satisfaction out of giving him oral. If that kind of sex play doesn't appeal to you then hand your partner this chapter and let him have at it. But assuming you do, here are a few tips on how to go from hair to there:

What's Your Objective?

A Trim Or Completely Hairless? It's totally up to you. Or rather, him. You might want a full "Brazilian" on him but he might have some splainin' to do in the locker room. Or you could do a combo platter—trim the pubes and shave the balls.

Tools

Buy A Dedicated Pair Of Scissors. Bacteria and yeast live in the groin—you don't want to spread these to other parts of his body. So don't use the scissors he uses to cut nose hair. He might end up with a boogers-to-balls yeastiness. Also, wipe down the scissors with rubbing alcohol, wash your hands and soap up his manhood. That will help create a sterile environment less likely to develop infection.

Buy Specialized Manscaping Tools. Try products like the Philips Norelco Bodygroom—a razor specifically designed to shave awkward places. Mangroomer also has some interesting products like a shaver with an "Extreme Reach" extension for those awkward, hard to reach places.

PUBIC HAIR

Cut It To The Same Length As The Hair On His "Love Trail." It starts at his chest and goes down to his tummy all the way south to that Access of Evil between his legs. Be consistent or he'll look like he lost a game of chicken with the lawn mower. If you want to go Brazilian and shave it all off, don't start with a razor blade. Start with a pair of scissors. Shaving long pubic hair can cause razor burn, itching or stubble. The hair can snag on the razor blade and cause a lot of pain. Also, pubic hairs are coarser and have more curl to them so it's easy for the hair to curl back into the skin and cause an ingrown hair.

Never Shave Upward Toward The Belly Button. Let's just say it'd be a rash decision. Shave horizontally and/or diagonally downward.

THE TAIN'T

Prop His Leg Up On The Side Of The Tub. *Carefully* shave the tain't ("tain't his balls/tain't his ass"). Don't shave too far forward or you'll end up with hairless racing stripes. I don't care if you're into NASCAR, *it ain't a good look.*

THE SCROTUM

Cut It Out. The hair, I mean. To about a half an inch with a pair of scissors. And if you'd rather shave all of the hair off...

Soak In A Warm Bath. It loosens up his pores, making it easier to get a close shave.

Lather Up With Shaving Cream. With the thumb and index finger of the same hand, pull the testicle bag's skin in opposite directions to flatten the shaving surface. Always start shaving with the grain. When you're done, do it again, only against the grain. Be careful! God gave men a penis and a brain but only enough blood to run one at a time, so you don't have much to waste.

Use Antiseptic Creams, Moisturizers And Baby Powder. Don't have him sportin' nothing but chaos down there to sproutin' nothing but redness. Moisturizing the area will reduce itchiness and irritation. Look for lotions with aloe or camphor.

Remember, giving "Richard" a makeover isn't something you're doing for your partner. This is something you're doing to maximize your pleasure during a blowjob. Speaking of "Richard," there are many so many versions of him across the land you'd think a rock concert let out. Some are circumcised some are not. Some are straight as six o'clock, some are curved like gravy boats. Some are big (yessssss!), some are small (noooooooooo!).

Let's unzip America's pants and see what it's working with.

PUTTING HIS PENIS
IN YOUR MOUTH

Chapter Five

What's He Working With?

You'll probably have more than one penis in your mouth over the course of your sexual career and you'll soon realize that there is a great diversity of dicks. Some are skinny and straight, while others are fleshy or have more curves than a scenic railway. Still others (LOTS of others) will have their foreskins attached.

Most American men are "cut," meaning that they've had their foreskin—the tissue covering the head of the penis—surgically removed. Circumcisions are usually made on the first or second day after birth. The custom for Jews is the eighth day. There are many ways to perform the surgery, but it basically works like this: The foreskin is "freed" from the head of the baby's penis by first grasping it with forceps, widening the opening, and then making a slit with a surgical knife. The slit is then separated and the foreskin is laid back.

Oy vey! Let's move on to happier subjects—like the benefits of having an uncircumcised penis. That's a much tastier subject.

As a culture, we believe that cut penises are more hygienic, even though there is no real supporting data. Some reports show circumcision lowers risks for infant urinary tract infections, penile cancer and possibly-maybe-but-nobody's-sure, sexually transmitted diseases. But come on, infant urinary tract infections aren't very common and penile cancer is extremely rare. In fact, the American Academy of Pediatrics was so unimpressed with the clipping crowd that in 1975 it recommended circumcision no longer be performed as a routine procedure because it wasn't medically necessary.

I'd love to blame the medical industry for cutting our foreskin and pulling it over our eyes but the truth is we're also to blame. We've turned circumcision into a fashion statement and disguised it as a medical need so we can feel good about it.

Most experts agree that the uncircumcised penis is more sexually sensitive. It makes sense if you think about it—the heads of most American dicks are constantly rubbing up against underwear (or if you go commando, denim), while our compatriots around the world get to wear protective sausage sacks. Well, no wonder uncut guys like Latinos are so passionate! They're feeling so much more than we are! Too bad we can't paste our foreskins back on. I'd do it faster than you could say "prepuce."

By the way all of the tips and strategies in this book apply to circumcised men (about 80% of American men) but since most of the world's men are NOT circumcised, there are special considerations and techniques to know when pleasuring an uncircumcised partner. I'll go over those in detail later in the book.

Overall, it's important to remember that because it spends most of its time sheltered by foreskin, an uncut penis is generally more sensitive than a circumcised one. It's best to err on the side of tenderness when you're first starting out, and pay attention to what makes your man moan and what makes him wince.

Why Is His Penis Darker Than The Rest Of His Body?

It's part of the sexual maturation process, but it's also because during puberty men discover a certain someone they'll shake hands with for the rest of their lives. Over the years, masturbation darkens the skin. Your skin would lose its sheen too if you shook it like a staff sergeant once or twice a day.

More Skin With Foreskin

Again, foreskin protects the head of the penis from rubbing, scratching, and scraping against clothing and that makes them more sensitive to the touch of your tongue or your hands. On top of that, anatomical studies show the foreskin has a rich concentration of complex nerve endings, adding to its sensitivity. That's why circumcised men only know five vowels while uncircumcised men know seven: A, E, I, O, U, OOH and AHH.

Uncircumcised men have to be more conscientious about cleaning their penis than their circumcised counterparts.

That's because smegma, a cheesy secretion, can form under the foreskin unless it's cleaned daily.

The extra skin that covers an uncut penis can be one of the most confusing parts of sexual anatomy. The very sight of it can send chills through inexperienced women, as they've likely had zero warning that it looks different from circumcised penises. In case you haven't seen one, the flaccid uncircumcised penis looks like the head is wearing a turtleneck. During an erection the head "pops out" of the turtleneck.

Penises That Curve Like A Gravy Boat

Few penises are as straight as uncooked pasta. Most have some degree of bend and a few have more curves than a racetrack. A curved penis can be a wonderful blessing during intercourse, as it's able to reach and stimulate parts of the inner vagina that go unexplored by a straight-on boner. But it can be intimidating during oral sex, given the logistics of your narrow throat. While most penises have some degree of curve to them, some have what would be considered irregular angles and some even have a "crooked" appearance, where the top part of the penis skews in a different direction from the base. Intense curvature of the penis is often attributed to "vascular trauma" that can be caused by rough sex, athletic activity or a physical accident.

Some curves are due to Peyronie's disease, a plaque build-up in the walls of the blood chambers of the penis. This plaque build-up forces the penis into a curve or bend.

The most basic and important factor in sucking a curved dick is positioning, and it may require you to explore the world beyond your knees. A guy with a dramatic upward curve might be easier to suck in the 69 position, while a penis that curves to the left or right might be more suckable with you on your side. Be open to trying a variety of positions that maximize your comfort and you may find one that lets the dick slide down your throat easier than lubed oysters.

A Drop in the Bucket

Ever notice that several drops of clear liquid ooze out of his penis when he gets an erection? It's called "Pre-ejaculatory fluid." About 30% of men have it. Sexual excitement squeezes the prostate and seminal vesicles and forces the fluid up (ranging from a drop to several drops). They serve as a built-in reservoir of lubrication. They also neutralize acid in the urethra from residual urine, keeping sperm safe for their journey to Eggland.

Penises With More Piercings Than A Dartboard

You probably don't have a metal detector installed in your mouth, but alarms are still likely to go off if a guy drops his pants and you see a pierced penis. Unfortunately, the popularity of genital piercing has not been followed by increased knowledge of how to navigate it once it's in your mouth.

Because of the low risk for complications and its relative simplicity, the most popular genital piercing for men is the Prince Albert, which is a ring or curved barbell that goes into the urethra and out the side of the head of the penis. It has a short healing time, too—six to nine weeks. Some piercings like the Ampallang or Apadravya can take up to 9 months to heal.

I know what many of you are thinking: WTF! Who the hell would go through that kind of pain? That is not what Beyoncé meant when she said, "Put a ring on it! I mean, some of those piercings look like they were hammered in by a Mexican roofing crew!

A flaccid uncircumcised penis looks like the head is wearing a turtleneck. During an erection the head "pops out" of the turtleneck.

It's a great question. Here's why guys do it: Aesthetics and the potential for increased sexual sensitivity. To some, a penis piercing is visually arousing. It often introduces new textures and sensations for both the owner and his partner. For the owner, additional friction around the head of the penis, which is already a pleasure center, can heighten sexual experiences. For the partner, a piercing promises the possibility of stronger orgasms during intercourse (they often function as a wonderful g-spot stimulant). Some women report that because of the piercing, they can actually tell how far in their partner is during penetration.

But not everyone is all that happy with their piercings. Men are in luck if their urethra is a sexually responsive spot, but out of it if it's not. The ring coming out of the urethra acts like a fan and spreads urine all over the place, so peeing can be a challenging problem.

And according to many piercing artists, the most common reason guys come in to have their piercing removed? Girlfriends complaining it hurt too much during sex.

THE SIZE OF THE PRIZE

Four Catholic ladies are having coffee together. The first one tells her friends, "My son is a Priest. When he walks into a room, everyone says, 'Father.'"

The second one chirps up, "My son is a Bishop. Whenever he walks into a room, everyone says 'Your Grace.'"

The third Catholic lady says smugly, "My son is a Cardinal. When he walks into a room, everyone says 'Your Eminence.'"

The fourth Catholic lady sips her coffee in silence. The first three ladies all ask, "Well...?"

She replies, "My son is a 6'2", hard-bodied stripper, and hung like a rhino. When he walks into a room, everyone says, "Oh, my God!"

It's time to tackle the elephant in the room (or is it a rhino?): SIZE. Men are far more obsessed with the size of their penis than women are. In surveys women don't even rank it in the top three characteristics they look for in a man. So if it generally doesn't matter to women, why does it matter so much to men?

We're going to spend a little time on the question of size because it is an extraordinarily sensitive subject for guys that can easily interfere with his performance and your satisfaction. You know how every woman it seems, even the skinny ones, think they're too fat? Well, a lot of guys, even ones named *Frankencock*, think they're too small. Every gender has its cultural curse.

Later, we'll talk about the accommodations you'll need to make for both a guy who's too small or too big (two sides of the same curse!), but for now, let's talk about why men obsess about the size of their dicks.

What Men Think When They Stand Naked In Front Of The Mirror.

Most men have a "bigger is better" mentality. I call it "Male Math": Size + Size = Status on Stilts. That's why men love bigger cars, bigger biceps, bigger guns, bigger wallets, bigger everything.

Add male misperceptions of normal-sized dicks to "Male Math" and you have a recipe for dick delusions. Here's what I mean: The only time heterosexual men see other erect penises is when they're watching porn, where every penis needs its own parking space. Even when they see other live penises in captivity (locker rooms) they suffer from an optical illusion that makes them feel smaller than everybody else. See, a penis on another guy looks bigger than yours because you're looking almost straight at his but straight down at yours. Angles make a difference. When you look down at something it always looks shorter than if you look straight at it.

Rounding out the follies, many men still believe that most women orgasm through penetration. So the more equipment you have to penetrate her with, the more sexually satisfied she'll be, right? Wrong. Seventy percent of women orgasm through stimulation of the clitoris, which is best done by a talented hand or a lubricated tongue. Preferably both.

Lastly, men have to survive locker room insult culture. Once, I was changing in the gym and I overheard this conversation between two friends: *"Hey, would you wear shoes if you had no feet? No? Then why are you wearing underwear?"* That's the kind of insult that can cast doubt even among the well-endowed.

Can You Tell If He's Hung By Looking At His Hands?

A lot of people think they can tell how big a guy is by looking at physical features like height, foot or hand size, or even voice depth. In reality, there is little correlation between these factors and penis size, so you can stop searching for clues and enjoy your soup!

Even seeing a penis in a flaccid state will give you little indication of how big it will be once erect, as some guys are "growers not showers."

So! Straight from the Department of Duh: The best way to tell if a man is hung isn't by looking at his hands, feet or nose. It's by looking at his erection.

My Kingdom For Eight Inches

What's fascinating about men's obsession with size is that they focus on length. But even when some women report that bigness is important (oh, you size queens!) they're talking about girth or as my girlfriend says, "Roundth."

At any rate, penile size can be measured in a lot of ways. Obviously, the differences will impact the results. There are two widely recognized ways of measuring the penis. The most common is the "You Wish" method. It involves looking at your pinky and seeing a thigh.

A Hilarious—And Accurate—Way To Tell If He Needs An Extra Large Condom.

Here's a clever trick a condom company came up with to determine if your man is well-endowed: Put a tube of toilet paper over his erect penis. If it slides all the way down to the base, he's average or below average.

If it gets stuck, then pop the champagne corks because he's one of the lucky few. Yes, FEW. Condom manufacturers estimate that only 6% of the population needs extra-large rubbers.

I'll talk about the second way in a second. First, the bad news: the average penis size is not six inches. The "six inch myth" got started when Kinsey did his landmark penis size study back in the 50's. Although there were 2,000 men in his study, it had a fatal flaw—the results were self-reported. Men were asked to go into a room, get themselves hard and measure themselves. Now tell me, would you believe anything coming out of a man's mouth while he's holding his dick?

Men always lie about size. Why do you think we came up with maps that associate an inch with a mile? Realizing that too many men were backdating their stock options, urologists developed a new way of measuring the size of the prize: A third party. So now every legitimate penis study includes medical staff doing the measuring and reporting.

And guess what happened? The average erect penis size shrank from Kinsey's 6.2 inches to 5.1 inches!

Now the truth is that different penis size studies show different results but NONE of the studies come anywhere close to the Kinsey study that popularized the six inch myth. Let's take a look at the latest *reliable* study as of the printing of this book.

The Journal Of Sex Medicine's Latest Penis Size Study (2016).

According to this study, the average erect penis size is less than six inches. And, read it and weep, African-American men don't have bigger penises than white men. Combine that with data from the Centers Of Disease Control (CDC) and I have some very bad news for the enduring African-American stereotype: Black men aren't bigger than white men in *any* department–not height, not weight, not BMI, and sadly, not penis size.

Hey, what's that sound? Reality cock-blocking another myth. Take a look at some of the eye-opening penis size stats from the Journal Of Sex Medicine and height/weight figures from the CDC:

Size Category	Black Men	White Men	Hispanic Men
Mean Length of Penis (in inches)	5.77	5.58	5.57
Mean circumference (in inches)	4.83	4.82	4.89
Height	5'8"	5'8"	5'6"
Weight	189 lbs.	193 lbs.	177 lbs.
BMI	27.1	27.1	28.0

Please note: The difference in length and circumference between the races is statistically insignificant. This study is relatively consistent with the results of prior surveys.

Can Guys Increase The Size Of Their Penis?

There is only one way to safely enlarge a penis: Lay it on my desk and I'll whack it with a hammer. You won't believe how big it'll get.

With the exception of the 2% of guys who have a "micro-phallus," every reputable medical association recommends against penis enlargement surgery. Most men who have the surgery end up with crooked, lumpy and deformed shafts, erections that point downward, and raw nerves caught in scar tissue and fluid that chronically collects around the testicles.

Contrary to the "male enhancement" emails we men get in our inbox, there's no way to "MAKE YOUR DICK BIGGER THAN A CLUB!!!" There's no pill, no pump, no enzyme that's going to give you "THE MIRACLE OF A 14-INCH HORSE COCK!!!! There's no surgery that's going to give you "MEATY 10-INCH SCHLONGS!!!!

Yes, I know most men would like to "ADD FOUR TER-RIFYING INCHES TO YOUR WANG!!!! But I'm afraid the only way they can do that is to borrow a porn star's dick for the weekend.

How To Handle A Guy With Size Insecurities

Some guys will be openly apologetic about the size of their prize ("I know things would feel better if I were bigger..."). Some may joke about it to reduce their stress ("You may have to squint when I drop my drawers") but most will simply drop hints about their insecurities. How should you handle it?

The same way you'd want him to handle any insecurities you might have about your body. When you ask your partner if your ass looks too big in those jeans, you don't actually want him to be honest. Otherwise you might hear him say, "I don't know, let me back up so I can take the whole thing in." No, you want him to LIE.

Similarly, if he asks or says something derogatory about his size, you need to LIE about it. Not like, "Oh, honey, you're hung like the Florida Panhandle." He'll never believe you. It's best to say something like, "I like the size of it. I wouldn't want it to be any bigger—it would hurt!" Or, "I love your dick because it's yours." Or, "I love your dick just the way it is."

Every good relationship requires fundamental acting skills.

What If He's Normal-Sized?

There's nothing more aggravating than a guy who's clearly normal-sized mewling like an unfed cat about the size of his dick. It's sort of like listening to your skinny girlfriend complain about being fat. You want to shake them both and yell, "Wake up and smell the pubes!" Well, sort of. The truth is, women aren't the only ones with body dysmorphia. Some men get it too. You can't undo their consciousness but you can inject some logic. For instance, tell your man what I said about angles making things look smaller: If men want to get a better indication of their dick size, they need to stop looking down and start looking in the mirror.

You can also suggest that he add an "optical inch" by trimming back his pubic hair. As I said before, the statue can be lost in the bushes. A little manscaping can make him feel so good he'll start saying, "It's not very big but I'm proud of every foot."

What not to say can be just as important. Never tease, even if it's good-natured ribbing. I have a girlfriend who was watching porn with her husband. She elbowed him in the ribs and said, "Now *that's* a cock!"

Not her finest moment.

For most normal-to-big guys, the single best way to manage penis size anxiety is to actually measure his penis and compare the results to the average of accepted studies.

So the next time he starts bitching, get out your cloth ruler and tell him to drop trou. If you want to show him his exact measurements, here is the scientific procedure that urologists use:

1. **Get him undressed in room temperature.** "Shrinkage" will occur if it's cold. I don't know about him, but I want every millimeter counted.

2. **Use a cloth ruler.** Tape measures or straightedge rulers don't measure curvatures well.

3. **Get him on his back and start where the base of his penis meets the stomach.** Do NOT start from the back of his balls. Nobody includes the basement when they quote the height of a skyscraper, so don't include the tip of his ass when measuring his mixed-use high-rise.

4. **Round up to the nearest centimeter**, not the nearest foot.

5. **Read it and rejoice.** Most men will fall somewhere near the average—below six inches. Check against

the Journal of Sex Medicine's size chart above to compare other stats.

WARNING: Do not attempt to measure his penis unless you're absolutely sure he's average-sized. Otherwise, you'll have to put the Suicide Prevention Hotline on auto-dial.

What If He's Hung Like A Gnat With Erectile Dysfunction?

It stands to reason that a significant number of men fall below the category of average. To some women, that might be a deal breaker (you size queens!) but to most it wouldn't.

There's no point in lying about how big he is when he's demonstrably below average. It's best not to say anything at all or keep it vague (*"I love everything about your body"*).

If he keeps bringing it up show him the results of the University of Zurich survey I wrote about in previous chapters—women pretty much don't care about size. You might also remind him of a survey in The Kinsey Institute New Report on Sex. It asked women which physical characteristics about men turned them on the most. Penis size came in fifth, after muscle tone, well-groomed hair, clear complexion and white teeth.

Does he want to turn you on more? Tell him to forget about dick size and get a better haircut.

Chapter Six

The Lips, The Tongue, The Skin Of Your Teeth

Your mouth has one distinct advantage over your vagina when it comes to delivering pleasure: The tongue. It is truly a marvel of the human body, and rarely do we appreciate its power to pleasure. In fact, the only people who seem to celebrate the tongue the way it deserves are taste testers, professional wrestlers and the odd circus act.

The tongue has over 10,000 taste buds allowing us to discern the marginal difference in flavor between a guy's jizz and Talenti's Sicilian Pistachio Gelato—while strangely enjoying (and sometimes craving) both! The brain is often touted as the most powerful sex organ in humans, but the tongue is a key that can unlock places the brain can't go.

One of the most remarkable aspects of the tongue as a sex organ is its versatility. It pulls off more tricks than a magician, and can be just as jaw-dropping as watching your beloved being sawed in half. The tongue can offer a soft caress or a firm massage; it can poke or tickle; it can take long, sloppy licks, or zero in on an area with devoted attention. The tongue contains eight different muscles, but, when relaxed, becomes one of the plushiest surfaces in the body. Appreciate the tongue's full potential in order to employ it most effectively, and make sure you let all of its talents shine during a make-out session or oral sex.

Kiss Me You Fool!

Aside from eating and speaking, kissing is the tongue's most important role in bed. As Confucius once said, "A passionate kiss is like a spider's web. Soon leads to undoing of fly." Wait, I don't think that's who said it. At any rate, the lips may get all the headlines in smooching but it's the tongue that transforms an innocent peck on the cheek to an intimate moment between the sheets. You can kiss your dog or your aunt with your lips, but the tongue is reserved for your Romeo. Remember the old adage: *A peach is a peach, a plum is a plum, but a kiss isn't a kiss without some tongue.*

Pucker up, baby!

It's difficult to have a great sex life without being a good kisser. It's kind of like trying to be a Hollywood socialite without releasing a sex tape. And you can't be a dynamite kisser if you don't have a tongue that is active, sensuous and adventurous. From soft butterfly kisses to junkyard dog lashes, it can penetrate your partner's lips, wrestle his tongue and explore every part of his mouth.

Here's a fascinating fact: Some researchers believe that saliva, which is produced in glands under and near the tongue, provides a primal "taste test" for couples, as it contains the DNA of every organ and gland in a person's body. There's evidence to believe that the flavor of your kiss can be affected by your genetic compatibility with a potential partner. Due to this, saliva operates as an individual's "signature flavor," according to Dr. Louann Brizendine, author of *The Female Brain* and *The Male Brain.*

When A Kiss Is Not A Kiss

A man escapes from a prison where he has been kept for 15 years. He breaks into a house to look for money and guns and finds a young couple in bed.

He orders the guy out of bed and ties him to a chair. While tying the girl to the bed he gets on top of her, kisses her on the neck, then gets up and goes into the bathroom.

While he's in there, the husband tells his wife: "Listen, this guy is an escaped prisoner, look at his clothes! He probably spent lots of time in jail and hasn't seen a woman in years. I saw how he kissed your neck. If he wants sex, don't resist, don't complain, do what he tells you, just give him satisfaction, no matter how much he ravages you. This guy is probably dangerous. If he gets angry, he'll kill us. Be strong, honey. I love you."

To which his wife responds, "He wasn't kissing my neck. He was whispering in my ear. He told me he was gay, thought you were cute, and asked if we kept any Vaseline in the bathroom. I told him where to find it. Be strong, honey. I love you too!"

How Do You Tell A Guy He Kisses Like A Pack Mule?

Does Mr. Right turn into Mr. Fright when he kisses? Some guys kiss like they're sweeping for land mines. You end up using your tongue as a flanking maneuver to stop the onslaught. How can you call a truce to your tongue wars and teach him how to kiss better without hurting his feelings?

Most guys are receptive to changing their techniques as long as you frame it as a request, not an insult. I would urge you not to say something like, "Look, you moron, you kiss like a pack mule and I'm choking on all the spit you're hosing down my throat." I mean, it worked on my boyfriend, but you need a certain finesse to get away with it.

Now, where was I?

Oh, yeah. Try this approach instead: "You know what really turns me on? When you do *this*. Then show him how you want to be kissed and say, "Now you try it."

Here are a few other tips:

> **Be rhythmical.** Move smoothly from passive to active, from slow to fast to back and forth, from dry to wet, to gentle and wild.

> **Breathe through your nose.** It prolongs the kiss.

> **Close your eyes.** They'll look like two giant beach balls to the guy you're kissing if you don't. And who

wants to kiss big balls? Wait. Bad example. Just keep your eyes closed and quit confusing me, dammit.

Make sounds. Small, almost imperceptible sounds. A tiny rumble here, a soft moan there. Communicate what you like and what you're feeling through noises, not words.

Kiss your partner's eyes. The heat of your lips on his eyelids will drive him crazy. Just make sure his eyes are closed. There's nothing worse than getting your corneas licked.

Let your desire show. Look at your partner with a deep, rapacious, insatiable hunger. The way oil executives do when they see the Alaska wilderness.

Adventures in Licking

No body part is as fearlessly adventurous as the tongue, diving into another person's mouth or simply trekking across your partner's body from head to toe. There's no need to limit your tongue's affection to just your man's mouth or genitals when there's a buffet of bodily flavors to taste.

Neck: You know how good it feels when your man makes his way toward your neck and begins to kiss, lick and slurp on it? Do you get goose bumps just thinking about the feel of his tongue running along the nape of your neck? Guess what? His neck has the same nerve endings as yours, so it's very likely that he would enjoy that type of romantic attention as much as you do. This might seem self-evident, although a surprising number of women don't employ "necking" during foreplay routines.

Don't be deterred if your guy has hair on his neck, as he can still feel the sensations. And if he's bearded, a little facial bush can help prepare you for some of the places your tongue will take you in the next chapter.

Ears: While ear lobes are pleasure points for both sexes, they're particularly sensitive on men, especially when your tongue is loving on them. In addition to the outer ear, there are nerve endings on the inside of the ear that can be aroused by the tongue. And if you really want to drive him wild, smack your lips in his ears. He will go crazy.

Ever find yourself getting fatigued after just a minute or two of giving oral? Let your tongue take over. With 8 different muscles it doesn't tire easily.

Do Tongue Rings Feel Better?

Guys don't generally like the feeling of metal on their penis, even when it's warm and wet from a willing mouth. It often brings more pain than pleasure if the woman is careless with how she makes contact with the penis.

So why is there a belief that tongue rings feel good to the recipient of a blowjob?

A combination of intrigue with how it looks and the supposition that girls who have tongue rings are just better at oral. But ask guys if they like blowjobs from girls with tongue rings and the likely answer will be "Not so much."

Nipples: How important are nipples to human beings? They're one of the first things nature takes care of when an embryo is formed, as nipples develop *before* a sex is determined. Once testosterone emerges in male embryos the nipples get "turned off" so they won't turn into breasts that can lactate. However, the testosterone doesn't "turn off" the pleasure receptors. Meaning, they respond to the same stimulation as female nipples. Circling your tongue around the outer rim of your man's nipple (the areola), and using the tongue to press the nipple down can make him harder than a frozen turkey.

Armpits: If you're squeamish about tonguing your guy's hairy neck, then brace yourself, because his pits might send you over the edge. But hear me out: licking your man's armpit is a win-win-win.

For him, exploring an area that is not used to attention or contact can often result in novel sensations.

For both of you, exploring a vulnerable area like armpits can increase sexual trust. Most guys are ticklish in that area. If you can transform the tickle into a pleasurable sensation he'll relax, but that will only happen if he trusts you not to tickle him. His trust, in turn, gives you more confidence and security to explore and arouse him. It's like surviving a national disaster or seeing any show with a Kardashian – the shared risk is a great bonding mechanism.

Feet: The feet have more than 7,000 nerve endings and your tongue can trigger almost every one of them, driving your man insane with lust. Start trailing your tongue along the bottom of his foot, and wedging it in between his toes, and soon you'll evolve to toe-sucking and practicing your deep throating on his paw. Just make sure he's clean. You don't want any toe-jam jamming your groove.

Is Sucking Safe?

It's exceedingly hard to quantify the risk for contracting sexually transmitted diseases through oral sex, according to the CDC. Is it high? Low? Nobody knows except to say that the risk DOES exist for gonorrhea, syphilis, herpes, HPV and to a much lower extent, HIV.

The only thing we do know is that oral sex carries a whole lot less risk than vaginal or anal sex. Scandalously, studies show that blowjobs are riskier than cunnilingus. In other words, going down on him poses a greater threat of STDs for you than it does for him when he's going down on you. Where is the fairness in that!

Other than wearing barriers like dental dams or using Saran Wrap during oral (Really? Who does that?) the best protection is intact skin and membranes. Make sure you and your partner do not have open sores or abrasions in your mouth or genitalia. It's important to never brush your teeth immediately before giving a blowjob, as it can create small wounds that grant access to your bloodstream. But even swallowing won't put you at risk for getting HIV or other STDs as the acids in your stomach destroy viruses on contact.

A Mouth Exercise That'll Help You Blow Him To Kingdom Come

Of course, the tongue isn't the only soldier in the platoon. It's surrounded by buddies that'll come to its aid. After reading each word below, draw your attention to that part of your mouth and focus on it for 5-10 seconds. Think about it singularly, as if it is the only part of your mouth that exists. Feel it warm up and moisten, and envision it coming into contact with a rock hard dick:

—Lips
—The tip of your tongue.
—The surface of your tongue.
—The bottom of your tongue.
—The insides of your cheeks.
—The front of the roof of your mouth (hard palate).
—The back of the roof of your mouth (soft palate).
—The back of your throat (uvula).

You should have this same intense awareness of each part of your mouth when giving a blowjob. Stay conscious of your lips, the roof of your mouth, and the back of your throat. You've got a wealth of pleasure-giving instruments in your mouth, so make sure each part is engaged throughout.

There's one part of your mouth not listed above but which deserves special mention: Teeth. Nothing ruins a blowjob like scratching or accidentally biting his dick. It is an epic party foul hard to recover from. Cover the teeth with your lips at all times.

The Tongue's Role In Making His Eyes Roll

It's time for the tongue to go to its final destination: the crotch. The tongue is a secret weapon in oral sex not only in the pleasure it provides to the guy you're sucking, *but in the relief it can provide to your mouth during a blowjob.*

Do you ever find yourself getting fatigued after just a minute or two of giving oral? That's because you're relying too much on your lips. Let your tongue, with all eight of its muscles, come to the rescue. It'll allow you to rest your lips while not interrupting the pleasure your man experiences. Tongues do not tire easily. Use that fact to your advantage.

The tongue not only has more lasting power than your lips, it provides a whole lot more pleasure. Your lips are pretty much limited to left/right and up/down motions. But ahh, the tongue, the tongue! It can move in any way it wants. It can also contort to different angles and shapes (enlarge the tongue by flattening it against his penis, roll it to lap up his taste or make it pointy it so you can dart in and out of crevices). The tongue covers a lot of territory in a short amount of time, leaving him with new meaning and renewed purpose to his life. And more importantly, giving you a variety of sexy taste and texture sensations.

Your tongue needs to be the Beyoncé of your blowjob routine: Twerking and stealing the spotlight every time it makes an appearance.

Chapter Seven

Bestowing A Bedazzling Blowjob

"Penises are always thought of as being so sensitive and powerful. And I get to put it in my mouth? It's so empowering to know that you have that much control over someone, and it's exciting to try out different things and see what makes them squirm. It's nice to be able to really please someone."

—L.

It goes without saying that men will receive pleasure during a blowjob and yes, of course, you will experience the "pleasure of pleasuring," but I want you to be a little more selfish than that. I want you to approach blowjobs as if they were meant to give YOU pleasure. Think of his satisfaction as an important marker of your efforts but more as "collateral pleasure"—something he gets as a consequence of pleasuring yourself.

One of the best ways of enhancing your own satisfaction during blowjobs is to become really good at giving them.

Competence breeds confidence which enhances self-pleasure. Word up:

> *"Plain and simple, I'm good at it and I know it. Which makes me enjoy it so much more making a guy squirm and moan. It's hot and turns me on hardcore. Plus it's fun and I could go to town on one all day long if I could. When I haven't done it for a while I start to get withdrawals and wishing I had a nice dick in my mouth to suck on. 100% my fave part of sex."*
>
> —Y.

> *"I'm really, really good at it, and knowing I'm making a dude squirm is pretty great."*
>
> —V.

> *"I love his whimpers of "Oh fuck. Oh my fucking god," etc. And, overall, it's something I'm really, really good at, so it's a huge ego boost for me."*
>
> —B.

As these women plainly understand, confidence significantly increases your enjoyment of giving a blowjob. There's only one way to gain confidence and that's to earn it through competence. That's why we are going to concentrate on improving your skills in this chapter.

Let me start by reminding you that we men are alarmingly attached to our penises. In fact, we love listening to "He's Got the Whole World in His Hands" when we pee. With the right kind of oral you can make your partner feel like he's got the whole galaxy in his hands.

Sending him into that galaxy requires four things: moisture, speed, pressure, and friction. Success starts with saliva. The most natural way of generating it is to bite into a sour apple or suck on a hard candy. Go ahead and buy some at the store. I'll wait.

Back so soon? Good, now bite into the sour apple. Notice how it makes you drool? It's your body's way of fighting off the acidity in the mouth (the saliva dilutes it). Of course, that's hard to do in the middle of unzipping him, so try this instead: Visualize biting into a lemon. Do it right now. Concentrate on the citric juices hitting your tongue and the sides of your mouth. Notice anything? You're salivating more! Conjure up that vision whenever your mouth starts getting dry during oral.

One of the best ways of enhancing your own satisfaction during blowjobs is to become really good at giving them. Competence breeds confidence, which enhances self-pleasure.

Your hand is the next most important thing. You need to deliver three things with it: friction, pressure, and speed. Use your hand as an extension of your mouth. Do this: Make a fist and punch yourself in the chest. Your knuckles should be touching your chest, with your thumb facing toward you. That's your starting position. With your hand in that position, twist/stroke on the way down and stroke/twist on the way up. You're basically doing a corkscrew motion as you wet him with a constant stream of saliva. Your mouth may give him moisture and heat, but it doesn't give him pressure and friction. That's what the hand is for.

If you can get these basics down—moisture with your mouth and speed, pressure, and friction with your hand—you're well on your way to mastery. Then it's a matter of add-ons, like pretending there's oxygen in his balls and making so many sex sounds the neighbors pull out their binoculars.

"I absolutely love giving blowjobs. Just the thought of satisfying my man is all I need in return. After he is done, normally I swallow it and I cuddle beside him. When I first started giving head I wasn't very good at it. But by him telling me what he does or does not like, and practicing on lollipops, I became a champ."

—N.

Now that you've got the big picture of bestowing a bedazzling blowjob let's dive into the details.

More On Moisture. Having a warm, wet, moist mouth is the single most important aspect of giving head. It will send him to Mars and back on a discount ticket. This can be problematic for some women as not everybody has a mouth moist enough to launch interplanetary trips.

How Much Saliva Does Your Mouth Make In A Day?

Brace yourself: 32 to 64 ounces! Think about that the next time you grab a half-gallon container of milk—that's about how much saliva you produce in a 24-hour period. Why so much? The slippery stuff—which is made mostly from water—breaks down food with special enzymes for easier digestion and lubricates food for easier passage down your throat.

Ever wonder why you wake up with breath so bad your dentist will only treat you over the phone? Because saliva production goes down to nearly zero when you're asleep, allowing odor-causing bacteria to build up.

Without a wet mouth, your lips tend to "tug" on a guy's skin rather than glide along, and you won't make it too far down the shaft before he expresses his discomfort. So, in addition to visualizing biting into a lemon, here are a few tips to keeping a mouth so moist "Richard" will think he's in a tropical rain forest:

• **Drink Water.** While staying hydrated may seem like a no-brainer when it comes to maintaining a wet mouth, it's something most people don't think about. If you know you're going to be giving your man head soon, start lubricating your mouth with water a few hours beforehand.

• **Chew Gum.** Get your salivary glands warmed up before you go down by chewing a piece of gum. It fools the brain with a signal that you're about to ingest food. Your mouth automatically starts moisturizing for what it thinks is the passage and digestion of food. Boy, is it in for a surprise!

The gum should have sugar in it, as there is a 10-fold increase in the flow rate of saliva when a sweetness or flavor is added to gum, according to the magazine *Dentistry Today.* It also has the ability to keep you three times wetter after you stop chewing. If you want to stay away from sugar look for gums with xylitol, which studies shows is an effective way of producing saliva.

• **Use Toothpaste And Dental Rinses That Contain Xylitol.** If chewing gum right before having sex gives you a trailer park vibe you're rather avoid, then brush and rinse your teeth with products that contain Xylitol, which is clinically proven to produce more saliva.

• **Suck On Hard Candy Before Sex.** You'll feel your

gums glisten as pools of saliva form under your tongue.

• **Yawn And Gleek.** Remember spitballs? You wet a small, balled-up piece of paper in your mouth and spit the projectile out to some schmuck? Yeah, me neither. Today it's called "gleeking," although without the paper.

To gleek, open your mouth as wide as you can, then touch your tongue to the roof of your mouth. Maintain this pose while you take a deep breath in and it will trick your mouth into yawning, which activates the saliva glands in your cheeks and underneath your tongue. In gleeking, the goal is to keep your tongue against the roof of your mouth, inhale and then spit with a forceful exhale that propels saliva from under your tongue. But you can skip that step and save the spit for the job ahead.

Use these tricks to turn your mouth into a virtual rain forest, and you'll be able to glide your lips from head to base, smoother than Tarzan swinging on vines.

A Word To Live By

A dim-witted brother and his brilliant sister inherit the family ranch. Unfortunately, after just a few years, they are in financial trouble. In order to keep the bank from repossessing the ranch, they need to purchase a bull so that they can breed their own stock.

The sister balances their checkbook, then takes their last $600 dollars out west to another ranch where a man has a prize bull for sale.

Upon leaving, she tells her brother, "When I get there, if I decide to buy the bull, I'll contact you to drive out after me and haul it home."

The sister arrives at the man's ranch, inspects the bull, and decides she does want to buy it. The man tells her that he can sell it for $599, no less. After paying him, she drives to the nearest town to send her brother a telegram to tell him the news. She walks into the telegraph office, and says, "I want to send a telegram to my brother telling him that I've bought a bull for our ranch. I need him to hitch the trailer to our pick-up truck and drive out here so we can haul it home."

The telegraph operator explains that he'll be glad to help her, then adds, "It's just 99 cents a word." Well, with only $1 left after paying for the bull, the sister realizes that she'll only be able to send her brother one word.

After thinking for a few minutes, she nods, and says, "I want you to send him the word 'comfortable.'"

The telegraph operator shakes his head. "How is he ever going to know that you want him to hitch the trailer to your pick-up truck and drive out here to haul that bull back to your ranch if you send him the word 'comfortable'?"

The sister explains, "My brother isn't too bright. He'll read it slow."

This story is a terribly long way of saying that "comfortable" is the most important word in giving good head. If you're uncomfortable, you're not going to deliver a lot of pleasure and you're not going to do it for very long. For this reason I want you to keep this in mind: *Your comfort is more important than his pleasure because his pleasure depends on your comfort.*

For example, a lot of women give head while kneeling on the bed with their partner on their back. You can't sustain that position for very long without feeling like a low-wage factory worker on the 11th hour of her 12-hour shift. The best positions are the ones that support you while giving access to a big part of your partner's body. Here are a couple of ideas that will make you feel "come-for-the-bull":

Both of you lie flat on your backs. He's on your left. You sit up and put your left arm over and across his belly (so your armpit is snug against his sides). Your back is to him but you have a grand view of his hoo-haw. The weight of your lower body is being supported because you're lying down while your left arm anchors you. This gives you leverage for more vigorous oral without taxing your comfort.

Him Standing Up With You Sitting On The Bed. You have total access to his body with your hands and you won't get as fatigued as when you're on his knees.

Him Standing Up Near The Edge Of The Bed With You Lying On Your Stomach. You don't have total access to his body with your hands as you do when you're sitting, but it's an excellent position for him to thrust it in and out of your mouth while you are in complete comfort.

You Sitting Up At The Head of The Bed Propped Up On Pillows. He stands over and feeds you. This allows you to use your hands as sex toys, delivering pleasure all along his groin, butt, stomach and chest.

Both Of You On The Bed With Him On His Knees and You On All Fours. The four-point resting position gives you the energy to carry on. Try a variation like yoga's "Child Pose" while he puts it in and out of your mouth. He'll love it because he'll see the contours of your beautiful back and tush.

I've highlighted a few positions that are demonstrably more

comfortable but that doesn't mean you shouldn't try other positions. Be creative and try out different positions. If it starts to hurt, simply shift to a more comfortable one.

So far, we've taken your partner on a slow roll along a beautiful countryside in a vintage car. Now it's time to kick the stand off the Harley, rev the engine and blow the carbon out. For that, we need to:

- Cover more area of the penis with your mouth.

- Use pressure and friction to stimulate the penis.

- Establish a rhythm and increase the speed to make the penis harder than the back of a bus stop bench.

Concentrate on giving the penis a full-length mouth massage. The objective here is to cover the entirety of his penis with your mouth (or as much as you can without gagging) while establishing a bobbing rhythm and increasing the pressure with your lips.

As your mouth descends on his hardness, flatten your tongue to provide fuller contact with the penis. It's warmer, moister and creates a better pressure seal. It also opens your vocal canal, allowing you to take more of the your guy's cock in your mouth. Remember: Grip with the Lips, and Flatten with the Tongue.

Your tongue should be in near-constant motion, massaging the underside of the shaft on down strokes and circling the head on upstrokes.

Depending on the size of your partner's penis (is it a taco? A burrito?) you're going to gag sooner or later. The trick is to know when you're getting close to your gag reflex and stopping before you get there. We'll talk about getting rid of your gag reflex in a later chapter but for now, simply avoid the trigger spot. It isn't pleasant for either of you. You'll cough up a lung and he'll have his pleasure interrupted. Nobody wins!

Speaking of nobody winning, let's talk about teeth. Don't. Ever. Do you know how a man spells "pain" when a woman uses her teeth? IN ALL CAPS.

Your comfort is more important than his pleasure because his pleasure depends on your comfort.

Let's Cut To The Uncut

A true paradox of the uncut penis is that the foreskin contains thousands of nerve endings that can drive a guy wild, yet it can prevent other parts of the penis from experiencing pleasure. You cannot give a proper blowjob to an uncircumcised man without pulling the foreskin back toward the base of the penis. If you suck an uncut penis without pulling the foreskin down, it leaves the head covered and neglected of most stimulation. It's like oral dry-humping, and if you've learned anything in this book, it's that "dry" is to a blowjob what "rough" is to cunnilingus—grounds for divorce.

Aside from not pulling the foreskin away from the head, the next most common mistake is *yanking* the foreskin toward the base. First, you shouldn't be "yanking" anything near a man's junk. Stimulating an uncut penis isn't like playing a guitar—you don't grab it by the neck and make it holler.

Rather, imagine "unrolling" the dick, slowly exposing the head. Gently tug the foreskin to the base of the penis but don't keep it there. Stroke it back-and-forth and you'll activate the nerve endings in the foreskin and the head of the penis. It's a double shot of pleasure, as he's going to feel your hand on his dick and a delicious sliding as the foreskin glides over the shaft and glans, alternately covering and exposing it.

"Blowjobs are part physical, part psychological. The real appeal doesn't come from the physicality of it for me, but for the fact that I know the sight of me with my mouth wrapped around his dick is something he'll have a mental snapshot of forever. Pretty sexy, right?"
—*P.*

Mastering the foreskin "tug and glide" is essential to unlocking your uncut guy's orgasms. In order for your man to fully feel the moist wonders of your mouth, you must *gently* pull back the foreskin in a back-and-forth motion. Did I mention gently? Because I meant GENTLY!

Notice: Some uncircumcised guys have a lot of foreskin and others have very little. The less skin present, the more gentle you should be when pulling the foreskin toward the base of the penis, as it will cause a guy a lot of pain if you pull too tightly.

Generally, the more foreskin a guy has, the more you can "roughhouse" with the foreskin. Try using your lips to gently nibble on the hood of your man's foreskin, tugging the skin toward your mouth. Directly or indirectly, he'll let you know whether that is something he enjoys, and if it appears to bring him pleasure, work your way around the foreskin using the same soft "bites" with your lips.

Some uncut guys also enjoy actual bites on the foreskin, but the possibility of your guy not liking it is great enough that you should either forget it or do it so softly that he doesn't panic and lift your face off him.

Studies show that sniffing his armpits will increase your libido, which will dramatically increase the pleasure you get out of giving oral.

When trying to understand how to pleasure foreskin, think of your nipples. Maybe you like your nipples licked and softly sucked, or perhaps you want a guy to gnaw on your tips like he's trying to untie a knot with his teeth. Either way, it can be agonizing when a guy gets it wrong. The same is true with foreskin. Some dudes can't stand any friction against it, while other guys don't mind if you nibble it just a little bit.

Fabulous Tip For Men Who Have Tips!

Once the dick is hard, position your tongue along the shaft or head of the penis while you have the foreskin pulled back. Then release your tug and let the foreskin roll over your tongue. He'll feel your warm wetness both on the underside of his foreskin and the surface of his penis. It'll feel so good you'll have him pronouncing all four "e's" in shit.

Techniques That'll Make Him Flail Like A Deer Trapped In A Minivan

Now where were we before we took a detour to uncut dicks? Oh, yes, using your lips! Use them to apply more pressure in the bobbing up and down from head to base. You can also increase the pressure by elevating the tongue to reduce room in your mouth and doing a "swallowing" motion that squeezes the tip of his penis.

STELLAR TIP! Sniff And Lick His Armpits. "Eeew," you might be thinking, but stay with me because you're about to say, "Ahhhh." This stellar tip is actually for you not him. Sniffing his armpits is highly likely to increase your libido, which will dramatically increase the pleasure you get out of giving oral.

How can that be? Neuroscientists at the University California at Berkeley recently made a breakthrough discovery: Sniffing a compound of male sweat called androstadienone causes hormonal, physiological, and psychological changes in women that result in sexual arousal.

Believe it or not, sweat is the main focus of research on human pheromones. For example, we've known for years that male underarm sweat improves women's moods and affects their secretion of luteinizing hormone, which helps stimulate ovulation. Androstadienone is a derivative of testosterone that is found in all body secretions, but it is in especially high concentrations in male sweat.

In the most recent trials, women were asked to take sniffs from a bottle containing androstadienone. Don't worry, they didn't gag. It smelled vaguely of musk. When compared to sniffing a control odor (yeast), the women who sniffed androstadienone reported significantly higher sexual arousal.

Stop! Throughout a blowjob session you should be asking yourself questions like, "What can I do that will turn me on more?" Otherwise, it will turn into a chore.

Researchers also noted an increased physiological response in women who sniffed the testosterone derivative. In other words, their blood pressure, heart rate, and breathing went up and stayed elevated for a full hour after the sniff test! The results of this study have been replicated numerous times.

So what does all this mean for you? If you want to raise your libido—and the pleasure you get out of giving him head—make sure you sniff and kiss his armpits. Don't sniff when the smell is so bad it could peel the skin off a battleship. Do it when it smells good. Sweat is naturally odorless. It only begins to smell when bacteria that live on the skin digest sweat and excrete waste. That's why sweat smells clean in the beginning and slowly turns into mustard gas. By the way, he doesn't have to sweat enough to water a lawn; even a dab will do.

I'm not saying that sniffing his pits will immediately make you want to yell, "Take me like a vitamin!!" The effects are far more subtle. But the research is solid and beyond question: Smelling androstadienone will change your mood and increase your sexual arousal.

"I love it so much my boyfriend will be talking about something (non sexual) and I will just unzip his pants and go to town. Then he will be like umm, what was I saying? Sometimes he gets mad because he was talking. Hah."

—M.

Stellar Tip! French Kiss His Glans

I want to let you in on a secret few women know: French kissing the head of the penis will give your man one of the most intensely pleasurable sensations he can have during a blowjob. Just put the head of his penis in your mouth and pretend you're French kissing his lips. Actually, there's no pretending because there *are* a pair of lips on the top of his glans—they are labia-like formations that cover the opening to his urethra. Use the same tongue strokes and head rotations as if you were kissing his mouth. Mix in some puckered-lip smooches and I promise you he'll be drenched in so much pleasure he'll be, well, tongue-tied.

When I've instructed my girlfriends to do it they each reported the same reaction—their partners either stopped the proceedings to ask "what the hell are you doing to make this feel so good!" Or they asked after the session was over. Here's why it's such a stunning sensation: When your tongue French kisses the head of the glans three things happen simultaneously—he feels the warm wetness of your mouth, the massaging action of your tongue and stimulation of an orifice most women ignore—the opening to his urethra.

This is your secret weapon, the technique few men have experienced. Do it and I promise he's going to want you more than he wants his next breath.

Hum Like A Beehive. It creates a vibration that adds a little step-shuffle-kick to great oral. Vibrations stiffen the penis. Why do you think so many men get horny during long drives? The car's vibration stimulates the groin area and next thing you know, the cobra rises out of the basket.

STOP! CHECK IN WITH YOURSELF.

We've talked a lot about using techniques to further his pleasure but what about yours? Remember, this blowjob is for you as much as it is for him. Throughout a blowjob session you should be asking yourself questions like, "How can I make this feel better for myself? How can I enhance the physical sensations I'm experiencing? What can I do that will turn me on more?" Actually, the most important question you can ask yourself is, "What can HE do that will give me more pleasure?"

These are not rhetorical questions—you need to answer them. Sometimes it's as simple as taking his penis out of your mouth so you can look at it up close and admire it. As a co-pleasuring activity you have the right to ask him to do what pleasures you. Would it be hotter for you if he gently moved his manhood in and out of your mouth? Then ask him to. Would it make you wetter if he talked dirty to you? Ask him to.

Don't know what arouses you? Make it up. Give yourself a pretend answer. You'll be amazed at how accurate you'll be. Pretending gives honesty permission to come out and play. If that doesn't help, try "what iffing" it. For example, you could say, "I don't know what would make this better, but what if I asked him to hold me in a way that I felt more safe and protected?" Or "I don't know what would turn me on more, but what if he moved his pelvis more rhythmically?" Or think about a woman you consider sexy and ask yourself, "What would she ask for?"

Our goal isn't to get you to *endure* a blowjob session. It isn't to white-knuckle your way until his climax. It's to enjoy the experience as much or more than he does! Remember, he may be the honored guest but you're the one throwing the party.

Move Your Head Back And Forth. You'll be adding a horizontal motion to go with your vertical up-and-downs. Delicious!

Take It Out Of Your Mouth Completely. It's important to regularly take your partner's dick out of your mouth and lick it a few times before putting it back in. Why? Because the temperature and moisture difference between being in and out of your mouth creates a series of hot/cold sensations that amplify his pleasure. More importantly, you'll rack up more pleasure points for yourself. Taking it in and out of your mouth will allow you to more fully experience his strength, length and "roundth."

Keep It Moving. Don't stay in one spot doing just one thing. If it's monotonous for both of you the pleasure starts decaying. When a guy goes down on you properly, he's kissing and licking you all over, not just concentrating on one spot. Same thing with good head. Suck the head, lick the shaft, kiss his balls, keep changing the pattern. *Except* when he's just about to orgasm. There is such a thing as momentum during sex and you never want to ruin the 'mo!

*"The act of giving head is awesome. I even love watching myself give head. Makes me feel sexy as hell. And plus, the **vast** majority of guys love receiving blowjobs, so knowing that I'm doing something I'm baller at that my partner loves is just fantastic."*

—J.

Nail It In. Here's a great sensation for your partner: Run your fingernails lightly along his shaft, balls and perineum. Did I say "lightly?" Because I meant LIGHTLY! Done right, it's a deliciously subtle way to make him squirm.

Befriend The Balls. So many women let the balls dangle all alone during oral sex, neglected and unstimulated. Sad! Licking and fondling your man's balls throughout a blowjob increases his arousal and pleasure, especially if you tickle the seam that runs along the middle of the scrotum. It's a sensitive hotspot known as the perineal raphe.

The balls are also a great odometer for how many miles you have left before your man ejaculates, as the scrotum will rise and contract the closer a guy is to climaxing. On the flip side, if you'd like to prolong the blowjob and prevent your man from coming, ease off on what you're doing and tug on the bottom of the scrotum to lower it away from his body.

You'll find more on pleasuring "the boys" in the next chapter.

Talk Dirty. Sex is terrific with taste, touch, sight and smell, but talk brings it all together. A four-cylinder engine will take you where you want to go but adding a fifth will get you there quicker and the ride will be more memorable.

Passionate sex is about creating and releasing energy. Talking is energy—in the form of noise vibrating in distinct patterns and pitches. You don't just hear sound, you *feel* it. There's scientific backing for this. Speaking or hearing sexually charged words is known to spike dopamine transmissions in brain chemistry, triggering sexual excitement.

French-kissing the head of the penis will give your man an intensely pleasurable experience.

Erotic talking is a release of pent-up energy. It gives voice to our innermost desires in ways that our bodies can't. It creates energy not just by the physical vibration or your emotional intent, but by prompting your partner to respond. Energy feeds on energy. Every word you say builds a step your partner climbs up on. And everything he says builds a step for you to rise. Keep climbing. Heat rises. Sometimes words get in the way but other times they *pave* the way.

Tell him how much you love him, how much you want him, but mostly how much you want his (hopefully) big, thick cock going in and out of your mouth. Dirty talk can make some women a little uncomfortable (you NASTY girl!) but it's a huge turn-on for guys. He loves football, right? Imagine him watching it without the sound. He'd cry. The game isn't the same without hearing the play-by-play.

Look In His Eyes. In sex, eyes aren't just the window to his soul; they're the portal to his lust, so look into his eyes when you're going down on him. The sexual charge takes the excitement to another level. Why? Because in his mind, you're not just sucking a cock, you're sucking *his* cock. It makes him feel special, like you don't want to taste just anybody's cock, only his. This, of course, is a complete lie, but as I said earlier, every good relationship requires fundamental acting skills.

While making him feel more special is a noble gesture on your part there is actually a far better reason to look in his eyes when your mouth is full of him—it will turn YOU on:

"I love the visual aspect of a cock disappearing into a willing mouth...and sometimes I envy the man because he gets to look down at his cock moving in and out between loving lips of a wanting woman. So, because I cannot see it from where I am...up close to all the action...I imagine how it must look to the man I am sucking...seeing it from his point of view. That turns me on BIGTIME!! I love when a man tells his woman to "look up" at him while she sucks

him...and I imagine that sight from his perspective.

Eye contact is so important for me during sex. Eyes are windows to the soul...so to look into them means to see more than just a cock...or a man...or a woman...but instead to see right through to what makes them who they are. That is something I find incredibly attractive when I am in love. I want to see inside the man, which allows me access to even his deepest, darkest secrets and desires. When I look up into a man's eyes as I suck his cock, my heart beats even faster and harder, making me hornier and wetter. To see a man's eyes reflecting the emotions he is feeling...the amazing sight he is seeing...the sensations he is experiencing...THAT stays with me and affects my every thought of him from that moment on."

—A. in www.literotica.com

Make It Sound Like There's A Half-Off Sale At The Liposuction Center

"Sex sounds" will make your head sessions feel like a manned moon shot. Along with talking dirty, the natural sounds of a wet mouth on a hard cock are especially appealing to men because it adds another dimension to the experience. Especially if you're in a position where he can't see you. What he lacks in visuals you'll more than make up with sounds.

Try an experiment on your partner: Have him turn his back to you while you pull up a porn video with a fantastic oral sex scene. Turn the volume up. The squelching sounds of hands and a saliva-covered mouth rubbing over a pulsing hard cock will bring him to his knees (and hopefully you too!).

Why are sex sounds such a turn-on? Because they amplify what you're seeing and feeling. It's easy to see why ambient sounds are important—because they can create emotions. For example, imagine making love in a room next to a construction site with all kinds of noise pollution—beeping backup trucks, jackhammers on concrete and strange men yelling at each other. Not terribly conducive to love-making.

Now pretend the room is outside a deserted beach with waves lapping at the shore. Big difference, no? Sounds don't just create an emotional state, they also give context to what you're doing. Ever driven an all-electric car? There's almost no sound from the engine. It's a little unsettling. Whether it's an electric vehicle or a hot man, you do NOT want to be in a position of wondering whether you've turned them on!

Prick His Pressure Point. You're kneeling between his legs. You spread his legs apart but with his knees bent toward his chest. You hold his dick in your wet mouth, bobbing gently while your hands find the middle of his hamstring muscles. Gently press one or two fingers into each hamstring (no nails please). Move your fingers a little to the left or right and press (trigger point locations differ slightly). Press gently at first and then with increasing pressure (but never enough to hurt). It's an incredible sensation.

Freshen Him Up With A Crescendo. This is actually best done before you start giving him head, as a gentle way to heat him up, but it's also a way to introduce variety in the middle of things. Lightly brush your hair against his body. It'll feel like feathers. Start with the chest and work your way down to his crotch. Then go down the side of his thighs, even to his calves. Work your way up to his crotch again. Dangle dangle on his dingle dangle.

Externally Stimulate His Prostate. Wait, how can you stimulate the prostate without inserting a finger into his anus? Because the prostate lays just inside the "taint." It's fairly easy to locate because an erection causes the prostate gland to swell to the size of a walnut. Gently reach underneath his scrotum and hold his testicles up. Using a well-lubricated hand (spit is *okay*, lube is better), gently run your fingers between half an inch and an inch behind the scrotum. You should be about halfway between the back of the scrotum and the anus at this point. The prostate will be about one inch below the rectum towards the scrotum.

As you stroke his penis (or keep it in your mouth), gently massage two fingers into the area. Try to move your fingers down and back, toward his tailbone. You will begin to feel a soft, but firm, spot. This is the prostate gland.

The prostate gland becomes very sensitive when a man is sexually aroused. It has a circular feedback loop: When he gets hard, the prostate swells up. Stimulate the prostate and you make his erection harder. Once he begins to orgasm, apply some pressure on the prostate and he will cum harder and with more volume.

And then you will have the keys to his kingdom.

Dealing With Difficult Penises

If your man's penis has more curves than a Coke bottle it may simply be impossible to get it in your mouth beyond an inch or two. While you should make a good-faith attempt to let his penis reach your throat, if you're unable to do so then it's clutch time for the tongue and lips. It's easier to explore and stimulate all parts of a curved penis with these two parts of the mouth, so send them into overdrive licking the head or massaging the shaft with your lips. Fit as much of the penis into your mouth as you can, and grip with your lips while letting your tongue go wild.

You're far more likely to brush your teeth against a curved penis than a penis that sticks to the middle of the road. Be conscious of that, especially during back-and-forth strokes.

Dealing With A Piercing? Grab it with your teeth and gently —gently!—tug it up and down, left to right and in circles. Ask your partner what feels good. Believe me, he knows. He's been playing with it a lot longer than you have.

Have you ever had metal clang against your teeth? Not a

good feeling. It's right up there with lightning strikes. Best to slow down the pace of your blowjob, using longer, more concentrated strokes. Take your time learning how the metal feels in your mouth, and soon it will be as normal as a standard blowjob.

And while you can develop into someone who can deep throat a Prince Albert, most guys with genital piercings aren't expecting you to take it all. Hell, nobody expects a sword-swallower to inhale the rod if there's a tennis ball attached to it.

Now that we've gone over most of the basic techniques about using your mouth as a living sex toy, I want to share a secret about men you might not know:

It's Hard For A Man To Orgasm With A Mouth-Only Blowjob

While every guy is different, many men find it hardest to cum while getting a blowjob compared to other forms of sex. For starters, most women aren't great at giving head (but not you—not after reading this book!).

But it's mostly because a blowjob wrests power away from a man in a way that other sexual acts don't. A guy has the most control when he uses his hand to pleasure himself. He can regulate the tempo and pressure of his strokes and time his ejaculation to occur with his most lustful thoughts. But he relinquishes all control during a blowjob. It's YOU that determines the speed, pressure, rhythm, wetness and friction. And unless you know your man really well, you're basically guessing at what will bring him to orgasm.

In addition, mouths don't cover as much surface area of the penis as his hand or your vagina or anus. The vagina and anus submerge the entire penis in warm, wet and gripping flesh, stimulating thousands of nerve endings simultaneously.

The bottom line is that a man needs a certain level of pressure, force and rhythm exerted on his penis that is almost impossible to attain with a mouth alone. If you've ever witnessed a guy getting close to an orgasm through masturbation you'll note how much stronger his grip gets and how much faster his strokes become. Once he reaches the point of "ejaculatory inevitability" the hounds are released and everything goes into overdrive. Again, this is almost impossible for a mouth to emulate. Fortunately, you have a body part that can lend you a hand.

All Hands on Deck

Your hands can form a tighter grip than your mouth and expand the contact surface on the penis. Think of them as an extension of your mouth, or at the very least, partners in pleasure. The hands create the pressure, friction and rhythm while the mouth and tongue provide the heat, moisture and lubrication. It's a partnership made in heaven.

There are lots of variations to hand-and-mouth blowjobs but if you master this particular one, everything else will fall into place. Do what I asked you to do earlier in this chapter: Make a fist and punch yourself in the chest. Your knuckles should be touching your chest, with your thumb facing toward you. That's your starting position. With your hand in that position, twist/stroke on the way down and stroke/twist on the way up. You're basically doing a corkscrew motion as you wet him with a constant stream of saliva.

Start slowly and gradually speed up while simultaneously gripping your hand tighter. As you reach the base start pooling saliva at the bottom of your mouth (visualize lemons, etc.) and as you get to the top of his head, lift your mouth completely off it and swiftly let the saliva spill on the top of his head as your hand corkscrews down toward the base and your wet mouth joins it. Congratulations, you've just lubricated his dick so that the corkscrew motion of your hands will feel even sexier.

What Speed Should You Use?

There's no one right speed. It all depends on the man and the mood. However, there is one general rule that applies to almost everyone almost all the time: *Start slowly and gradually build up speed.*

How much speed you build up depends on what your partner enjoys. How do you find out? Ask him! Or watch him as he masturbates and take mental notes of his style. Once you understand how different speeds affect your partner's experience you'll be able to figure out which speed is appropriate for each stage of your encounter.

STOP!
CHECK IN WITH YOURSELF AGAIN.

The guest at the party seems to be having a great time but what about the host? How are <u>you</u> doing? Did you remember to ask yourself those all-important questions—How can I get more physical pleasure out of what I'm doing? How can I make my body feel better? How can I enhance the physical sensations I'm experiencing? What can HE do to make it more stimulating for me?

Is he too passive? Ask him to be more active. Is he too silent? Tell him to vocalize his feelings. Would stimulating your clitoris help? Try it. What if <u>he</u> stimulated your vagina? Ask him. Again, he may be the guest of honor but there is no point in throwing a party if the host isn't going to have a good time.

Go Gradually Faster & Gradually Slower.

You can spice up a blowjob by suddenly changing up the speed of your bobs and strokes, but don't use a "Stop/Start" technique too much because frequently changing your thrusting pace is likely to throw off your partner's rhythm. Fluidity and flow are your goals, not any preconceived notions of the "right" speed or depth.

Your partner isn't going to be an innocent bystander in the proceedings. If he's any good (God willing) he will not just simply lay there like a crash test dummy that just had a big helping of wall. He'll change positions, move you around and be an active receiver. If he doesn't, and you think it will turn you on (trust me, it will) ask him to be more active. For example, he could prop you up against the headboard and "feed you" his cock. Then, you could pleasure yourself as you feel his strength and hardness moving gently in and out of your mouth. Prioritize your pleasure and I promise it will increase his own.

Taking It To Pound Town.

Generally speaking, you can bring a guy to climax with faster strokes than slower ones. This is because almost all males like an increase in speed and pressure as they approach orgasm. Watch him masturbate and you'll see what I mean. As he gets closer to the detonation, his grip strengthens and his strokes quicken. And, if he's like most men, he'll orgasm looking like Jerry Lewis being electro-cuted.

The Unforgiveable Sin: Changing The Stroking Pattern When He's Close To Coming.

Whatever you're doing the instant you sense that he's going to come is what you should keep doing until he completely ejaculates. Now is not the time to try a different position or change the depth or speed of your strokes. The reason is simple: Never interrupt momentum. Ever notice that during masturbation men don't change their stroking pattern as they near the point of no return? They might grip it with more pressure and increase the speed but they don't fundamentally change the stroke, say from tight and fast to loose and slow. Keep that in mind as you're blowing him. If he's showing signs of an approaching eruption while you're pumping him slow and deep, continue pumping him slow and deep. Do not fundamentally change your stroking pattern unless he says, as many men do, "Faster! Harder!

At that point you have a wet, and may I add, sticky decision to make.

Spit, Swallow Or Cry?

"I have no problem with giving a blowjob until my job makes him blow," a girlfriend once confessed to me. Semen is indeed an acquired taste, whether it's sliding down your throat or splattering against your face. Some women are born with a love for its taste and texture, while many others bemoan the messiness.

Like alcohol or caviar, the macho gazpacho rarely tastes good the first time you swallow it, but like many things in life what starts out as an abhorrence becomes an obsession.

"Anyone who tries coffee or red wine for the first time discovers that it is an acquired taste. But over time as the beverages are associated with a stimulating lift or a pleasant buzz, one enjoys the taste more and more.

Eventually, one starts to crave it. Likewise, while I didn't enjoy my first gulp of semen, over time I associated it with my lover's joy and adoration, as well as my own arousal and orgasm.

Eventually, like Pavlov's dog salivating at the sound of a bell, the smell, taste and texture of semen became something that I actually enjoyed...to the point of actually craving it."

—V. in Quora.com

I Scream, You Scream, We All Scream For Mancream.

Whether you like the taste, texture, look and smell of semen depends on how you interpret its release. If you ascribe no other meaning to it than a simple biological process—like peeing—then you are going to like it about as much as you like masturbating with a cheese grater. The bleachy smell, the oysters-going-down-your-throat feel and the knowledge that it came from deep inside your partner's body will probably make you blanch.

But if you perceive semen as an elixir of masculinity, the very embodiment of your man's essence, a symbol of the sacred fire burning within him, then you're going to be turned on by swallowing it or feeling it on your skin. You're going to experience it as a form of taking communion. Life-giving communion, actually. After all, it's filled with millions of sperm that in another time and place (your vagina) would produce life.

"For me, the greater my love for the man, the greater my fascination with his cum. Now I love to smell it and lick the little droplets of pre-cum off the tip of his cock. I love the feeling of accepting his 'offering' to me like a reward for my efforts when he finally cums."
—A. in www.literotica.com

Milking It For All It's Worth

What's in the milky white stuff anyway? For the most part, semen is made of sugar, water, enzymes, protein, zinc and citric and ascorbic acid (Vitamin C). There's not enough of anything in it to cause harm or good. Here's the breakdown:

- Only 2% of semen is actually made up of sperm (that's why men don't notice any difference in semen volume after they get vasectomies).

- About 5% of women are allergic to semen (the poor dears)

- The average man ejaculates about a teaspoonful or two of semen

- The average ejaculation has 12 calories.

- There is enough sperm in pre-ejaculate to impregnate women. That's why "pulling out" just before you ejaculate doesn't always work.

"Spitters Are Quitters": The Case For Swallowing

What could be more intimate than sharing the "essence" of someone you love? Sex is about coming together, becoming one in an intensely pleasurable encounter. It's about communion, merging, sharing. It's an act of love. Swallowing is a way of showing how much you want him to be a part of you.

Some women are obsessed with swallowing because of the meaning they've ascribed to it. Some feel not just connected but "owned." It can feel like the ultimate form of surrender —to have his seed 'planted' in you.

To others, it's a kind of trophy they put on their psychic mantle. It isn't about surrender but about conquest ("I made him cum and now I know what he tastes like"). And to others, it's simply about feeling special—after all, how many other women are walking around with his semen inside them? Wait, given the nature of most men, that's probably not a good question to ask!

Here's Mud In Yer Eye!

Watch your eyes! The average speed of a man's ejaculation is 28 mph. Interestingly, that was Olympian Usain Bolt's fastest run ever recorded. Meaning your guy's jizz could win an Olympic gold!

The velocity of a man's ejaculation is believed to give the semen a head start on its journey toward a woman's egg, since once it's released, the sperm travels at a leisurely pace of 6 inches per hour.

Some historians point to intriguing evidence that some of the most ancient Christian sects, known as "Gnostic Christians" used semen as the sacramental wine of the communion. There are even more ancient rituals in which the ingestion of semen was considered the drinking of Life Itself.

There is also a kind of spiritual dimension to sharing semen. A deep tongue kiss with jism in your mouths can "seal the bond" and springboard you into a deeper dimension of intimacy.

Of course, not everybody sees it that seriously. One girl-friend says, "*I love swallowing because it tickles as they wiggle going down.*"

Does Diet Affect The Taste Of Semen?

Hey Michael!

Remember that famous scene in that early 2000's classic comedy *Sex & the City* when Samantha complained that her new boyfriend had "funky-tasting spunk"? Well, I'm in the same pickle. I love swallowing semen but not when I have to choke it down like foul medicine. One weekend my boy-friend and I went away and I did all the cooking, preparing only the foods that are supposed to improve the taste of semen. The result? Awful. I found something I lost years ago—my gag reflex. Is there anything I can do to make his cum taste better?

—Hollerin' about swallowin'

Dear Hollerin':

Semen is produced in the reproductive tract, not in the digestive tract. Changing what you eat to improve the taste of your semen is a little like changing your toilet paper to improve the smell of your shit.

The prevailing thought by people WITHOUT medical degrees is that dairy products, which contain a high bacterial putrefaction level create the foulest taste. That and asspsaragus. And no that's not something the spellchecker didn't catch. I sexualize everything, including vegetables.

Here's what I DO think has a chance of working: Water. Since urine and semen pass along the same tube, it makes sense that semen would be somewhat tainted by residual urine. If you drink a lot of water (and you should) your pee will be crystal clear and less likely to skank up the slank.

Dark, highly concentrated urine, on the other hand, is likely to put the funk in the spunk. It doesn't matter what foods you eat, your urine will be dark if you don't drink enough water. So stick a hose down his throat and turn the faucet on before he sticks his hose down yours and turns your stomach sour.

Final Thoughts About The Big Gulp

The vast majority of men want to see you swallow their load, but you are not obligated to do it. I typically categorize swallowing under the tension every couple struggles with in balancing the need to respect boundaries against the expectation of adventure. These imperatives often come up against each other and it's up to each individual couple to negotiate things out to their satisfaction. Personally, I think you should only do it if you think it's going to advance *your* sexual gratification.

Of course, the only way you're going to find out is to try it. But beware this business of "I'll try everything once. " It's bullshit, at least when it comes to sex. My philosophy is to try everything three times. The first time you'll get it wrong, the second time it'll feel strange and the third time it might feel nice.

> *"There's something really sexy about making your partner writhe and moan and feel good. I've never had an issue with any smells, tastes or anything like that. Semen isn't the most pleasant thing I've ever had in my mouth, but as long as I swallow it pretty quickly it isn't an issue."*

> —K.

If you're determined not to swallow, don't worry. It's fairly easy to avoid because most men give you clear signals when they're close to ejaculating. Their cock becomes harder, their breath quickens and their thrusts become faster. And most will tell you that they're getting close.

For heaven's sakes, do not, under any circumstances, simply stop what you're doing because you're afraid that he might cum in your mouth. Imagine how you'd feel if the guy stopped licking your clitoris just when you began to orgasm? You'd be like, "Say hi to the curb for me!"

If you feel him getting close to climaxing, pull your mouth off and keep stroking him with your hand until he comes. You won't get the silver or the gold, but hey, bronze is a medal!

If you can't read the signals (some guys are remarkably calm when they ejaculate) or he stays silent, you can still avoid it by being clear upfront. Tell him that you don't want him to cum in your mouth and to warn you when he's getting close.

Why Does Semen Go From White To Clear In Minutes?

There's a wide variety of consistency and viscosity in semen, but for the most part it comes out white and then turns clear. Here's why: The two glands that make up most of the liquid in semen are at odds with each other. The seminal vesicle contains sugars and proteins that cause semen to coagulate, turning it white. But fluid from the prostate gland contains enzymes that break down that coagulation. So basically, his ejaculate doesn't know whether it's coming or going. So it does both. It coagulates as soon as it leaves his penis, then immediately goes into "liquefaction."

If you have to take one for the team (either by accident or because you simply want to please him) it's best to look on the bright side of having to swallow or receive a facial:

1. It's usually a small amount to have to deal with.

2. Semen is loaded with proteins, nutrients and few calories.

3. At least this encounter with cum didn't lead to a pregnancy!

And if it does end up in your mouth, just spit it out on a towel or the sink without judgment. Don't make a face like the cat just died, or spit it out like it's poison or reenact the Death Scene From Camille. You'll just make your guy think you don't like him very much.

Okay, everything we've talked about so far is going to make you a competent partner, but if you really want to be a sublime lover you need to make him forget the universe exists outside of your lips and tongue. And that can only be done with an approach I'll describe in the next chapter.

Chapter Eight

The Peacock Technique

"My favorite part is having my guy squirming and unable to string two coherent thoughts together."

—K.

"I love to hear him make little sounds and moan and look at him in the eyes. So sexy."

—M.

"I love how he sucks in his breath when I move my tongue a certain way. Or when begs me not to stop. It's an incredible rush."

—L.

The most powerful sexual organ isn't between your legs or between your teeth; it's between your ears. As important as skills are to the end result, they will fall flat unless they're guided by a vision of sex that's beyond the physical. Let me clarify this with a guiding principle about memorable sex:

It's not what you do to him. It's where you take him.

All the skills, tactics and techniques you've read so far will make you a competent lover, but if you want to be a peacock among common poultry you need to have more than skills. You need the ability to transport him into a different plane of existence. And in order to do that, you have to understand how to create an agonizing joy called anticipation.

Anticipation is the feeling of excitement about something that is going to happen. I'm going to show you how to capitalize on this feeling to deliver (and receive) maximum pleasure but first let's talk about how anticipation works. I give you two scenarios:

> **Scenario 1:** You walk into a friend's home and she immediately waves a plate of delicious home-made chocolate chip cookies under your nose. "Eat, EAT!" she says. So you do.

> **Scenario 2:** You walk into your friend's home and she waves a plate of home-made chocolate chips cookies under your nose. "Smell," she says. You reach for one and she says, "Not so fast! We have to wait for the other guests to arrive." She puts the plate right in the middle of the table so you're constantly looking at its chocolaty goodness, salivating and fantasizing how good they'll taste. Finally, the guests come and she offers you one.

Which cookie tastes better?

Almost everyone will say the cookie under scenario #2. Why? The cookies have exactly the same ingredients. The answer is simple: Anticipation amplifies pleasure. It creates so much excitement, activates so many nerve endings that things taste better with it than without it.

It's the same thing with blowjobs. If you want him to have the experience of the chocolate chips in Scenario # 2, learn how to build anticipation. The object is to keep your partner's body in suspense by only delivering an aspect of what he's expecting (the way your host did by letting you see and smell but not touch or eat the cookies). This builds desire and curiosity, keeps your guy eagerly anticipating your next move and makes him crave you more. By the time you're done, the sexual encounter becomes more intense and satisfying (just like the cookies).

Robin Skynner, the great psychiatrist, once famously said, "Anticipation is the central ingredient in sexual desire." His studies proved that "Sex has a major cognitive component —the most important element for desire is positive anticipation."

Anticipation is an emotion that mixes enthusiasm, pleasure, excitement and anxiety toward a longed-for event. Like having your girlfriend's mouth on your cock. Wait, did I say "anxiety" in that earlier sentence? Why would anxiety figure into sexual anticipation? Because there is always some concern that the highly anticipated event will not occur. Let me explain with a concept called "Suspense and Resolution."

We experience suspense/resolve cycles all the time; we just haven't necessarily labeled it as such. For example, the high-schooler dying to find out if she got accepted to her preferred university. The letter arrives. SUSPENSE. She rips it open and reads the answer. RESOLUTION.

It's nearly midnight and the host is tearing up the envelope for best movie of the year. TENSION. She announces the winner. RELEASE.

It's match point at Wimbledon. The champion you're rooting for just missed her first serve. She tosses the ball up in the air to hit the second serve. ANXIETY. It clears the net and lands inside the service box. RELIEF.

Always prolong the tension of a blowjob the way a maestro holds a note on the piano ... and then resolves it with a satisfying chord.

For our purposes, there are two pillars to a suspense/ resolve cycle. First, is a longed-for event. Second, a lack of knowledge about whether the event will occur. Let's apply this to a couple having sex for the first time. She's kissing his body from chest to stomach. She's headed south. For him, there's a longed-for event (her mouth on his cock). There's uncertainty about whether it's going to happen (he doesn't know if she likes to go down). SUSPENSE. She kisses the inside of his thigh. TENSION. She kisses his balls. EXCITEMENT. Finally, she puts her wet mouth on his raging hard-on. AHHHHHHHHH.

Notice what happened here. Tension amplified the gratification. The anticipation of satisfaction allows the man to get greater pleasure in the final gratification. Imagine if the girl in the above scenario immediately blew him before he could even get his pants off his ankles. Yes, it would still feel good, but would it feel as good if she had held back in the way a maestro holds a note on the piano—and then resolves it with a satisfying chord? I think not.

As I see it, there are three types of "Oh My God!" a man can say when he's in bed with a woman:

1. OMG, I'm in heaven

2. OMG I'm in hell

3. OMG, where am I?

A suspense/resolution approach to your blowjobs will give him OMG #3. It'll feel so good he'll lose track of time, space and place. So how can you use anticipation to create an energy loop that carries your partner further up the sexual vortex?

Introducing The Peacock Technique

Are you ready to light him up like an all-night liquor store? Then get ready to do some "peacocking" (named because you don't show him the feathered glory until the very last moment). There are four parts to the Peacock Technique: Tease, Lure, Escalate and Resolve.

Every technique you've learned in this book should be put through this prism. Let me explain by starting with a simple goal: Putting your mouth on your partner's erect penis.

During a typical blowjob a woman might, after a nice make-out session, wander south and put her wet mouth on her partner's dick. While no guy would complain about that, in my mind it just makes her, ahem, common poultry. To become a peacock one must activate the Tease-Lure-Escalate-Resolve model.

Here's how it works. Instead of simply putting your moist mouth on his dick, you do the following:

TEASE

Moisturize his mind before moisturizing his dick. As you're kissing him in the mouth, wander over to his ears. Kiss them dryly at first, then warmly blow on them as if you're fogging a window, only gently, silently. The heated moisture will drive him nuts.

While "fogging his ears" say things like, "I can't wait to kiss your cock, to feel the thickness of it filling my mouth." Then s-l-o-w-l-y caress a wet tongue around his ear and snuggle it in his ear drum. Go in and out slowly. He'll picture his dick going in and out of your mouth.

Do you see what you've done here? You've filled him with anticipation. You've waved the hot cookies under his nose. Every nerve cell in his body awaits your next move.

LURE

Wiggle your way down his body. Assuming his clothes are off, give him dry kisses all the way down, from his neck to his nipples to his belly.

Now your mouth is right next to this dick but it's not touch-ing it. Use your hand to get it harder and harder. You've lured him into thinking you are about to give him head but instead you come up and "fog" his ear again. This time you ask if he wants you to put the throbbing dick you're gently pumping in your hand into your wet mouth.

When he says yes (or rather "YES, YES, FOR THE LOVE OF GOD, YES!!!!"), go back down his body alternating with shallow and dry kisses. Touch his balls and play with his dick but *lightly*, as if you're only concerned with the con-tours of his genitalia. Slowly kiss his balls and smell his manscent. Start giving him small, wet kisses from his balls all the way up the shaft and when you get to the head, pretend you're about to put it in your mouth and *STOP.*

Hold his dick by the base and the shaft for a glorious few moments of torturous anticipation. Stroke his balls lightly while holding his shaft and pool the saliva in your mouth by visualizing biting into a lemon or doing the "gleek."

In the meantime, you've built up so much anticipation that his entire body is on high alert as it prepares for sky-high joy. He doesn't know that you're pausing to fill yourself with saliva. He's thinking, "Is she going to put it in her mouth? IS SHE? IS SHE?!!!

Tease, tease. Lure, lure.

ESCALATE

At this point your mouth should be filled, brimming with warm, wet saliva and NOW you're ready to put the head of his dick in your mouth. Do it suddenly and without warn-ing. Be sure to have the title of his mortgage, car and stock portfolio at the ready because when he feels that warm moist mouth he is going to sign everything over to you!

Hold his dick in your mouth without moving for a few moments (however, let your tongue do some French kiss-ing) and then when he's acclimated (his moans and groans subside), start hands-free bobbing up and down.

RESOLVE

When he gets acclimated to the hands-free bobbing (again, the moans and groans weaken), make an O-ring with your index finger and your thumb, tighten the grip and start moving up and down in short distances—about an inch be-low the corona of the head to just past it. The combination of the saliva acting as lube, and your fingers increasing the pressure at the most sensitive site of his dick will send him to a higher level of pleasure.

Why is this part called "Resolve?" Wouldn't climaxing be a resolution? Yes, but there are different levels of resolution. If your goal is to give him head, then bobbing up and down on his dick is one resolution. If your goal is to make him cum that would be a different resolution. A resolution, for our purposes is YOUR end point, your goal, not his.

For example, if your end point is kissing him deeply, then the "resolve" is a French kiss. The Tease, Lure, and Escalate would be whatever creative ways you come up with to enhance the anticipation before your tongue does its good and dastardly work.

Let's take a look at another example of The Peacock Technique.

The Sloppy Diamond

Put your partner on his back at the edge of the bed where you can kneel and have access to his whole body. Picture a line drawn from his cock to his right nipple to his mouth to his left nipple and back to his cock. That's the diamond path your mouth will travel.

TEASE

Start by sucking the head of his cock gently. He's now thinking he's going to spend a long time in your mouth. WRONG. After maybe two or three bobs go to his right nipple and suck on it 2-3 times with big wet kisses, licks and nibbles (oh, you tease!) Now, he's thinking, okay, a little nipple action. WRONG.

LURE

You now go for his mouth and give him 2-3 very wet, long kisses. Notice how you've lured him into thinking you're going to do one thing and then you do another.

TEASE AGAIN.

At this point he's thinking, "WTF! I have no idea where she's going!" Exactly. And because he doesn't know, his senses are heightened and your very unpredictability makes everything feel like, well, those chocolate chip cookies you can smell but can't eat.

Now, follow the diamond line and go to his left nipple and pay devoted attention with your tongue.

ESCALATE

Go back to his cock. What'll really make him grab the sheets is when you start varying how you go down the diamond path of his hot zones. For instance, going from his cock to his mouth back and forth, ignoring his nipples. The inability to predict builds anticipation. So be unpredictable. While your traveling down the diamond path with your mouth, your hands are free to double his pleasure. You can, for example, put a left-hand finger in his mouth while stroking his balls with your right. While kissing him you could caress his face. While sucking on his nipples you could stroke his inner thighs. This is when you start having sex Tivo style: Play...fast forward...slow motion...stop...rewind...play.

RESOLVE

Speed up the process (get to the different parts of his body quicker) and build momentum. Finally, settle exclusively on his cock and instead of giving it 2 or 3 long bobs before moving on, use the "O-ring" technique mentioned earlier and keep doing that for a while. He will go radioactive with pleasure.

Why it works: The Sloppy Diamond builds anticipation ("when is she going to suck me off?"), provides action and energy (moving between different parts of his body), lures him into thinking he knows where you're going, supplies variety (stimulating different erotic zones) and resolves tension (by settling on his cock with O-ring motions).

Let's Review

Increasing anticipation increases sexual pleasure. Lowering anticipation lowers pleasure. Ever had sex with a guy who skips the warm kisses and tender caresses and just tries to stick it in you? That's an example of no anticipation creating no pleasure.

Here's another example of anticipation's importance in creating pleasure. Think about your favorite drink. I prefer a chilled chardonnay around 7 pm (only on days that end in "y," however). Around 4 pm I start fantasizing about the golden liquid behind a chilled glass teasing me with its droplets of condensation. The anticipation actually changes my physical state. When I actually pour the nectar of the Gods into a glass at 7 pm and put it to my lips it's clear: My anticipation of a longed-for event heightened its ultimate pleasure.

This is what you should be aiming for in all your blowjob techniques: building anticipation, providing action and energy, supplying variety and resolving tension. In other words, TEASE, LURE, ESCALATE, RESOLVE.

Why dust him with the feathers of ordinary fowl when you can transform him with the spectacular plumage of a peacock?

Chapter Nine

What Are You Supposed To Do With The Twins?

"If it has tires or testicles there'll be trouble."
                    —Polish proverb

Testicles are like martinis: one's not enough, two's just right and three's too many. The vast majority of men have two testicles, unless they were born with a birth defect or suffered injuries.

The scrotum is the sack that holds the testicles, which produce sperm and testosterone. The muscles in the scrotum are affected by temperature. When it's warm, the scrotum and testicles hang lower. When it's cold they sit tight against the skin and sometimes even disappear into the body.

Testicles are *extremely* sensitive. No doubt Mother Nature made them that way to remind men to stand guard over their precious jewels. Of course, Mother Nature is a post-op tranny. What else could explain the fact that she made testicles the genetic equivalent of female ovaries? The same sack of cells that become testicles in men become ovaries in women. The testes actually rest inside the pelvis during fetus development and descend before birth.

Testes is Latin for "To Testify." Instead of placing their right hand on the Bible, early Romans put their hand on their testicles while bearing witness in a public forum. I can only imagine the judge asking, *"Do you swear to tell the whole truth and nothing but the truth, so help your balls?"*

But I digress. Let's answer a question that keeps every guy in suspense during oral:

What Are You Going To Do With Those Balls?

Hopefully, a lot. They are exquisitely sensitive to touch and if you're serious about delivering Ritz-Carlton level pleasure you will pay devoted attention to them. First, a little on why men's scrotums are so sensitive. One, they lack protection in the form of bones, large muscle mass and fat. Two, they have a ridiculously high number of sensory nerve endings, so every touch, no matter how minute, carries noticeable sensations. A good rule of thumb is to treat them like grapes, so don't apply *any* pressure let alone the kind that would turn grapes into wine.

Why Is There A Line Going Down His Penis And Testicles?

All men have it. It's a sort of "seam" on the underside of the penis. It forms when the fetus is in the uterus. In women, the seam becomes the vagina's inner lips. In men, the seam encloses the urethra along the length of the penis.

The Cup & Coddle

Ball Handling 101 starts with cupping the scrotum in your hand. The warmth of your hand provides half the pleasure (and helps loosen the scrotum skin, making it more sensitive to stimulation) while the rest of the arousal comes from applying *slight* pressure or a *tender* tightening of your grip around the sack. Familiarize yourself with the feel and movement of your man's balls by finger-juggling the scrotum, as if you were working Chinese meditation balls.

Am I Nuts?

An African-American man was the subject of his family's harangue one holiday as they sat around the family dinner table. "Why don't you bring girlfriends home for the holidays?" asked one sister. "Or get married or have kids?" asked his brother. Thinking he was ashamed to bring anybody home because he was only attracted to white girls, his mother said, "Ya'll, maybe he just doesn't like chocolate." The son replied: "Oh, I love chocolate. I just like mine with nuts."

Pinch & Roll

You're probably familiar with the pinch-and-roll method since it's a popular way to stimulate the labia. Technically, the scrotum skin is nothing but a labia infused with a Y chromosome, so treat it with love and respect, but mostly kindness. The elasticity of the scrotum skin makes it one of the most pliable parts of a man's body. Whether a guy's sack hangs loose or taut, use your thumb and index finger to apply small, *gentle* pinches on the scrotum, then roll the skin between your fingers, manipulating the soft tissue to maximize your man's satisfaction.

Tug & Squeeze (Lightly, Please!)

Some dudes are super sensitive in the scrotum region and don't enjoy any tugging, while others (not many!) like a little more aggressive play. The majority of guys fall in the super-sensitive category, so it's best to start out with a gentle tug and gauge how your man responds. This is not the time to practice your hand-ball techniques.

Blow air on his nuts after you've moistened them with your saliva. He'll experience a refreshing coolness that tickles the flesh.

Use your thumb and index finger to form a ring around the base of the scrotum where it attaches to the body. It's not essential that your thumb and finger tips connect, but you want to grip as much of the scrotum as you can for ideal pleasure and comfort. Gently tug the scrotum away from his body to make the skin around his testicles stretch tight, which exposes more of the scrotum's nerve endings than when it's in a relaxed state.

Why Do His Balls Move By Themselves?

Hey, Michael!

One day I was staring at my boyfriend's balls after he came and realized they were moving by themselves. At first I thought it was because he had just ejaculated, but they move by themselves whether we've had sex or not. Do they have a life of their own? Why do they move?

—Movin' on up...and down

Dear Movin':

The movement is called "testicular circulation"—blood coursing throughout the scrotum via internal streets and avenues known as veins and arteries.

When his balls are practically doing the tango with each other it's because of the cremaster and dartos muscles. They move testicles in and out like the line outside my editor's bedroom.

Remember, testicles are sperm factories and they're heat-sensitive. Sperm need to be kept at a certain temperature or they'll start dying like flies in a jar—slowly and painfully.

When the "boys" get cold, they snuggle up and get

warm. When they're hot they hang lower than the scruples of a homecoming queen looking for her next bump.

Ever notice how just before orgasm, his testicles get into a lock-and-load position? That's the cremaster and dartos muscles working it hard.

Want to try a cool experiment? Make the boys dance. Next time you're in bed with a guy (and if you're like the rest of my readers, that should be in about 10 minutes), touch the inner portion of his upper thigh.

Watch closely as his testicles move in the direction away from where your hand is touching. It's called the cremasteric reflex, which keeps the boys out of harm's way. When the "threat" is over, the testicles will come back to whatever position they feel safe in.

Do the 'W'

Now that your mouth has made contact with the balls, let's pivot to learning how to pleasure your guy's scrotum with your tongue. Lick the balls or let them rest on top of your tongue as you juggle from one to the other.

A good way to start licking the balls is by lying on your stomach with your face toward his crotch, then use the tongue to trace a 'W'—gliding down the left side of his ball sack, going up-then-down in between the balls, then finishing with an upward lick along the right side of the scrotum.

This easy technique makes sure every part of the scrotum receives attention, warms your guy up for more physical contact with his balls, and helps you get an idea of how sensitive this region is for him. For an extra electrical charge, use the "Gleek" technique to flood your mouth with saliva then deliver it with a flattened tongue on his scrotum. You'll cover a wider area and make him believe the world is ending slower.

Give Him A Hum Job

Place one or both of your guy's testicles in your mouth, use your lips to gently tighten the grip, then begin to hum—either by stretching out your normal moans, or with a focused hum that would put a smile on a Tibetan monk. The nerves just beneath the scrotum skin are especially receptive to vibrating sensations. Alter the "verbal massage" by adjusting the timbre and tempo of your hum. Slow the pulsating down by using a deep-pitched hum or increase the rate of vibrations with a higher pitch.

The nerves just beneath the scrotum skin are especially receptive to vibrating sensations, so place his balls in your mouth and hum. It'll feel like a verbal massage.

Breathe & Relieve

Ironically, almost no one blows during a blowjob, but blowing air is an important part of your arsenal. Here's a fantastic trick that'll have him scrunching the sheets: Blow air on his nuts after you've moistened them with your saliva. He'll experience a refreshing coolness that tickles the flesh.

Your mouth is a multi-convection fan, so don't limit its output to a cool stream of air. For another type of sensation, hover your gaping mouth above your man's scrotum, then use the back of your throat to push out a blast of hot air on the balls, which relaxes and loosen the skin, and makes the scrotum more receptive to stimulation.

Fire & Ice

While we're experimenting with temperature and its impact on arousal, let's bring in some outside props to make the fluctuation in temperature even more dramatic and stimulating. Place an ice cube in a paper towel or other thin wrapping, then slowly rub the cube across your man's scrotum. You'll likely see a physical reaction to the cold temperature as your man's scrotum tightens toward the body in search of heat. Save the testicles a trip upward by removing the ice pack and using your mouth to heat the scrotum. The contrast between coolness and warmth will unlock unique sensations hard to reproduce when the scrotum maintains a constant temperature.

Why Does One Ball Hang Lower Than The Other?

Just like half of all women have labia minoras that are longer than the labia majoras, most men have variations in size between their testicles. On average, testicles grow to be about 2 to 3 inches in length and 1 inch in width. The left testicle is smaller and hangs lower in 65-85% of men. Interestingly, scrotal asymmetry is faithfully reproduced in Greek sculpture.

We don't actually know why one (usually but not always the left) hangs lower but the prevailing theory is temperature regulation. Twin testes, hanging at equal heights, would create too much sperm-killing heat. The more exposed surface area in the scrotum the cooler the temperature, keeping the boys strong for their upstream swim. Hanging at slightly different heights prevents them from crushing and overheating each other.

Tea Bags Fly Free!

We've already covered one type of tea-bagging, where you insert your man's scrotum into your mouth for a hum job, but there is more of this type of pleasure to be had. Introduce yourself to the unique pleasure of the scrotum's soft flesh caressing your facial skin. You can experience some unique sensations by letting your guy rest his balls on your face or nestle them in your eye sockets (with your lids closed—nothing worse than getting a pube in your cornea!). When your BFF calls to ask how your night went, you can honestly say, "I had a ball!"

Two, actually.

Lastly, I want to show you how important the twins are to a man's climax: If your guy is having trouble "finishing" through oral or manual stimulation, show a little love to his balls and I promise you'll see the same sign on him that you see on movie posters: "Coming Soon."

Chapter Ten

Issuing A Gag Order On Your Gag Reflex

"Go Bananas!
Go, Go Bananas!
First, you lean to the left
Then you lean to the right
Then you peel the banana
And HUH! Take a bite!"

Are you frustrated that you can only take a couple of inches of your partner's banana before you start gagging? Are you scared of being choked to death by "Frankencock?" Are you adventurous and want to see if you can "deep throat" guys (put their erect penis into your mouth all the way to the base)?

There's only thing stopping you: Your gag reflex. About one in three people have no gag reflex (a lot of them are undoubtedly porn stars!). But quite a few have a hypersensitive throat. Never mind big penises, they can hardly swallow pills.

The Soft Palate Can Cause A Hard Stop

The hero and villain of any deep throat session is a part of your mouth known as the soft palate. Hero because this spot makes the head of the penis feel like a million bucks pre-tax; villain because this is the spot most likely to cause gagging.

To locate the soft palate do this: Take your index finger and put it inside the roof of your mouth with the palm facing away from you. Glide the finger along the roof of your mouth for about an inch. Notice how hard and relatively unforgiving it is? That's the hard palate. Keep going and you'll notice a distinct change in the feel of the palate. It becomes much softer. That's where the soft palate begins. The hard palate contains bone so do NOT bang your guy's penis against it during a blowjob—it does not feel good! However, the soft palate is muscle and tissue coated in mucus membranes and a penis will feel dreamy up against it.

Play cupid by introducing the head of your guy's penis to your soft palate and you'll soon discover that it's a match made in heaven. The soft tautness of your throat around his throbbing head can send you both into an almost transcendental euphoria, where you can feel his pulse beating inside your throat. But only if you train your gag reflex. Otherwise, it's going to be a real pain in the neck.

Unfortunately, the soft palate frowns upon deep throating, since touching it with any object (especially a dick) typically triggers your gag reflex. So the question becomes, how in God's pajamas are you supposed to put an over-sized kielbasa down your throat without coughing like a Kentucky coalminer going up the stairs? Fortunately your gag reflex can be trained into submission so that even the most shallow of throats can swallow the longest of swords.

How To Get Rid Of Your Gag Reflex

The best way to avoid gagging is to stop a hard penis from going past the hard palate into the soft palate, but really where's the fun in that? By spending just a few moments a day with the process you're about to read you can substantially reduce your gag reflex and enjoy years of unencumbered head without so much as a muffle. Here's how to do it:

Desensitization.

The process of desensitizing your soft palate is, without question, the most effective way of diminishing and sometimes getting rid of your gag reflex. The process gradually acclimatizes the soft palate to being touched in deeper and deeper areas without triggering the gag reflex. Here's how it works using a toothbrush:

- Find out where your gag reflex starts by touching the tip of your tongue with the head of a toothbrush. Now work your way back by touching deeper parts of your tongue. It won't be long before you, *COUGH, COUGH, COUGH* find the trigger point. There it is! Keep the head of the toothbrush right there. Yes, you'll gag but only for a few moments. Slowly, you'll stop gagging as your body realizes it's not in danger. Once you can comfortably keep the head of the toothbrush in that spot for about ten seconds without gagging, lightly brush the spot for a few seconds.

If you're still gagging choose a spot closer to the tip of your tongue and start there.

- In the next few days go to the exact same spot and repeat the process. Notice how you're gagging less and less. Once you're no longer gagging at all...

- Touch the toothbrush about ¼ to ½ inch further back from the spot where you used to gag. This is your new starting point. Hold for ten seconds. Now brush.

- Go to the exact same spot and repeat the process until you no longer gag. Keep moving the toothbrush further back over the next few days. Do you see what's happening? Your gag reflex is being desensitized. Keep moving farther and farther back until the toothbrush touches the soft palate.

- Now touch the toothbrush to the soft palate and repeat the process, only don't brush. It'll hurt!

Be persistent and don't rush. For desensitization to take hold it must be done slowly and over time. This whole process should take you about a month. But think of the prize: Swallowing foot-long hot dogs.

With relish.

Thumb Clenching

This is a popular dentists' trick that distracts your brain. Lifehacker.com cites a study showing it is effective in tamping down a gag reflex. All you have to do is make a fist with your left hand and clench your fingers around your thumb. The top of your thumb should not be visible. Put a fair amount of pressure on your thumb. If you want to test it, put a right hand finger down your throat as you clench your left thumb. You may notice a pronounced decrease of your gag reflex. Why does it work for some people? Scientists think the pressure may simply be distracting enough to stop you from gagging.

Apply Pressure To Your Hegu Point

According to the same Life-hacker-reported study, putting pressure on the Hegu point can hold off the gag reflex. The Hegu is the concave soft point between your thumb and index finger. Pinch it hard and it can relieve the gag reflex.

One of the reasons deep throating is so impressive is precisely because so few people can do it. It is a sexual title that must be earned.

Apply Pressure Between The Chin & Lower Lip

This too seems to diminish the gag reflex. You could get your partner to do it but that's a serious commitment to what amounts to a sexual parlor trick. It may be more work than it's worth. Still, it's an option.

Numb your soft palate.

You can use a numbing throat spray to desensitize the soft palate, or a gel that's normally used to relieve tooth pain. The effects should last for about an hour.

As you can see, you have several options to load more cargo in your mouth. These techniques will help you tame your gag reflex for routine blowjobs. But if you want to earn a black belt in oral—deep throating—you need to learn a few more things, especially if your partner is hung like a club-tailed dragon.

Before we talk about those techniques, a question must be asked...

Should You Deep Throat A Guy?

All those who believe in psychokinesis, raise my hand. No? Okay, all those who believe they should deep throat a guy raise your hand. Okay, now slap yourself with that hand. Deep throating, or taking an erect dick so deep into your throat that your lips touch the base of his penis, is difficult for almost everyone. You should not attempt it without first training your gag reflex. More importantly, you should not attempt it unless you think it will bring *you* pleasure, never mind him.

I would highly discourage you from trying to deep throat if, during routine blowjobs, you cough and gag like you just took a killer bong hit. You should make no apologies for not trying or even not wanting to try. Sometimes a girl's gotta do what a girl's gotta do. And sometimes a girl's gotta put her foot down on a dick.

Besides, you can give unforgettable oral without making the rabbit disappear completely into the hat. Now, having said that, there is one good reason to try: The challenge. One of the reasons deep throating is so impressive is precisely because so few people can do it. In a sense, it is a sexual title that must be earned. For example, anyone can straddle a guy and call herself a cowgirl. It takes little skill to bend over and please your man doggie style. Likewise, any girl can put her lips around a penis to earn a rose, but only an elite few earn the title of deep-throater and they're usually in the ring ceremony.

To be sure, it doesn't count if you're deep throating a guy whose penis is so small he can make it disappear by breathing in and out. Deep throating a four-inch penis is commendable, but not particularly impressive. It's like winning a daytime Emmy. Generally, at least six inches are required before you can pat yourself in the back and say you accomplished something. Let's take a look at what it takes to stop dicking around with the bronze and go for the gold.

The Upside Of Choking

When a penis gets lodged in the back of your throat the body instinctively starts choking. What may surprise you is that gagging can help your ability to give head. As you gag, the throat begins to lubricate itself in the hope of dislodging the foreign object and that lubrication is in the form of saliva.

That is one hell of way to give a wetter blowjob.

Team Throat

While the throat is the star, the lips and tongue are the executive producers, fluffers, grips and every other supporting crew member that makes the production a success. In addition to the massaging talents of both, the lips will help you wrangle the increased slobber that deep-throating uncorks, while flattening the tongue is key to unlocking the depths of your throat canal.

And while we're doing an inventory of the parts of your mouth it's important to stay conscious of your teeth while you're attempting to deep throat. Your chompers are more exposed the wider you stretch your mouth, and your jaws will instinctively clinch down when your gag reflex is poked. Talk about stealing victory from the jaws of defeat!

Why Do Guys Like Deep Throating?

Imagine for a second that you're a penis: You're toiling the day away, hour after hour, in dark and cramped quarters. And your only company is a couple of nuts and a real ass-hole. You'd be pretty stressed at the end of your day, what with your muscles aching and in need of relaxation.

Getting a blowjob would be the equivalent of sliding into a hot, soothing bath, while getting deep throated would be like sinking into a Jacuzzi, your every worry melting under a rejuvenating massage.

The pleasure guys derived from deep throat is multi-dimensional, encompassing the mind, body and spirit:

Physical: It's not hard to understand why having their penis immersed in a warm, wet crevice would be physically enjoyable for guys. A deep throat session provides fuller contact between the mouth and penis, stimulating nerve endings along the shaft and head simultaneously.

While the entire dick gets affection when it's being deep throated, it's still the head that is the most sensitive part of a guy's penis. As the head goes further into your throat, the passageway narrows and turns silky, providing a soft gripping massage that will release every ounce (and drop) of stress your man has inside him.

Pride: Having a big dick is important to most men even though most don't have one. If a man could exchange 20/20 vision for a foot-long penis, or promise to breathe less oxygen each day in exchange for a couple of extra inches, every fraternity and sports team would be filled with partially blind asthmatics.

It's tough for a guy to get objective, quantitative affirmation that he has a big dick, since most guys don't go around comparing penis sizes with their friends. If he hears you gagging on his manhood he'll interpret it as the most authentic, unfiltered confirmation that his cock could re-conquer Rome.

Intimacy: Deep-throating can inspire tenderness from your partner. Plenty of guys appreciate what it means for a girl to welcome all of him inside her mouth, and they show it by becoming more affectionate than usual, which in turn allows you to relax and swallow him even further.

Why Would A Girl Like to Deep Throat?

For the challenge. For the power. For the feeling. Let's take a look:

Physical: In *Deep Throat,* the seminal movie that erected new sexual norms in the 1970s, Linda Lovelace plays a sexually dissatisfied woman who goes to a doctor who discovers her "throat clit." While that may sound like the corniest of plot lines, there's evidence that women can indeed experience a kind of oral orgasm while deep throating. The back of the throat is connected to the vagina via the vagus nerve and the massage a penis provides to it can stimulate sexual sensations. By the way, "Vagus" means wanderer—the nerve wanders through the body from the brain to the throat all the way to the cervix, uterus and vagina.

Pride: Being able to deep throat might not be the type of thing you brag about to grandma, but it's still a talent worth celebrating. There's a certain sexual swagger that develops in those who know their mouth can tame the meanest of cocks and fulfill their man in a way that others can only fantasize about.

Power: Counter to the common misperception, the person doing the sucking holds all of the power during deep throating. You determine how wide to open your mouth, and how far the penis penetrates it. You decide whether to stroke your man's ego by gagging for relief, or crush his spirits by effortlessly swallowing his penis like a baby carrot. You determine whether to take control and regulate the pace. Hell, you're in control of whether deep throating happens or not!

Intimacy: Being relaxed is an essential part of being able to deep throat as it's hard for your throat to expand when you're filled with tension. Deep throating your guy is one of the most intimate gifts you can offer him, but it can also tap into your spirit. According to Tantra philosophy, the fifth chakra is located in the throat, providing the gateway to your truest expression.

Pick Your Position

While a common position for oral sex is the girl on her knees and the guy standing over her, this is not the ideal stance for a deep throat session unless the guy has a downward curve to his penis. You should always account for the shape and angles of your man's cock when identifying the best positions for blowjobs and this is especially true if you want to deep throat him.

The most effective position for deep throating is lying on your back with your head dangling off the bed.

The most effective position for deep throating is lying on your back with your head dangling off the bed, which automatically flattens your tongue and expands your vocal canal. With this position you surrender some control to your partner, but what you lose in sexual power you'll gain in oral depth.

Open Wide & Say "Ahhhhh."

Here's an interesting way of relaxing your gag reflex while his penis is entering your mouth. Pretend your doctor is about to use the tongue depressor on you. Say "Ahhh." This opens the throat and gives the doctor a wider view of your throat. It also provides a bigger canal for your partner's ship to pass through. Once you say "Ahhh" your mouth will be ready for the other half of that religious affirmation: "Men."

Another great position for deep throating is "69," where you align your bodies so that each person's mouth is on the other's genitals, simultaneously performing oral sex. Every inch of his purple mountain majesty gets easier to swallow as his lips and tongue rub against your lady parts. Just remember to be careful. Even if you subdue your gag reflex, it is exceedingly hard to breathe when a dick is that far down your throat. You don't want to go from dying for dick to dying from it!

Chapter Eleven

The 20 Most Erotic Blowjob GIFS And Videos

One of the things that might stop you from fully realizing a blowjob's sensual potential is that the majority of images and videos you've seen are either off-putting or centered exclusively on male pleasure.

And even when you see gifs, pics and videos showing female pleasure in the context of oral sex, *it is a man's version of what female pleasure should be.*

Let's face it, 95% of porn is made for men and it tends toward "raunch culture" with its explicit subordination and coercion of women. Men act as if they are sexually-entitled and owed sex on account of their maleness. Women are portrayed as weak or submissive. It's often degrading and the pleasure flows only one way—to the male.

Even when male-made porn doesn't portray men as sexually-entitled boors and women as submissive weaklings who sound like wounded animals, there is very little emphasis on female comfort, desire or pleasure. Most of the time when you watch a porn video it's obvious that the women in it are not turned on.

A porn star once asked me, "Do you know the difference between fucking and making love?" Before I could answer he said, "Making love is something a woman does as a man fucks her." Blunt and ugly, that pretty much sums up the state of porn.

Yet, porn can be an amazing tool for women, if you find the right ones. You can use made-for-women porn as a sex toy; a sort of visual vibrator that can make you feel good in all sorts of ways. I believe very much in imagery that sexually empowers women. To that end, I set off a team of women to scour the interwebs for images and videos showing women actually enjoying themselves while giving blowjobs.

To my team's disappointment, it was unbelievably hard to find those images and videos but in the end we succeeded. We took the hundred or so that passed our quality test and then put it to a vote among a panel of women to choose the very best ones.

The result is a magnificent collection of gifs and videos that show how pleasurable giving a blowjob can be. Notice how comfortable the women are, how sexually satisfied they are, how much fun they're having. To me, these images get to the very heart of this book: Seeing blowjobs as a way for women to gain sexual satisfaction, not merely provide pleasure to their partners.

Enough. It's time to stop reading and start gasping. Allow me to present...

The 20 Most Erotic Blowjob GIFS And Videos

Links:
Callmemaybe.us/gifs
Callmemaybe.us/videos

PUTTING EVERYTHING ELSE IN ITS PLACE

Chapter Twelve

How to Milk Your Man With Your Hand

A hand job: The 21st century equivalent of the kiss.
—Urban Dictionary

To guys, hand jobs are like a Pepsi: not your first choice, but you'll take it. Still, there's no reason squeezing one out with your hands should feel like a consolation prize for him. If the beverage he wants is unavailable, don't give him a Pepsi —give him a Jack & Coke!

While using your hand to get a guy off may seem like an easy, mindless form of sex, it actually can be quite difficult to bring him to orgasm. After all, he's spent years in the masturbatorium, so he's an expert at getting himself off. He knows exactly what he needs to "burp the baby" and you probably don't.

Puberty is a time when nature says to boys, "Shake hands with Mr. Penis." And then it says, "Ok, you can let go now!" And of course, he never does. Not for long, anyway. His dick and his hand are *very* well acquainted. They know each other's quirks, rhythms and most secret desires—whether he likes a straight up-and-down motion, circling the head, or has some weird Morse code-type sequence of jerking that unlocks his orgasm. Because he's grooved a pattern into his body I have a DUH-level secret to giving great hand jobs: *Take mental notes as you watch him masturbate to completion.*

Think of it as learning how to cook a great meal. First, you ask the chef how to do it and then you watch him, and then you take matters into your own hands. It saves you hours of burnt bread, cracked eggs and culinary scowls. On the subject of hand jobs, almost any guy will tell you: *"Nobody does me better than I do."* So, sit (or kneel) by the master and learn.

How To Put Him In The Palm Of Your Hand

Today's sexually active teenage boys are fond of saying, *"A hand job is a man's job, a blowjob is your job."* But what do teens know about sex other than doing it badly? The true hand job *artiste* (that would be you) knows that a hand job, done correctly, can actually be an immensely gratifying experience for a guy. Just because men can do it themselves doesn't mean it becomes an outsourced job if you do it. Quite the contrary. Do this: Kiss the inside of your wrist. Now get your partner to do it.

Which one felt better? His, of course! We are fairly dull to our own nerve endings, but when somebody else stimulates them? BOOM! Same with hand jobs. Which do you think feels better to him—your hand or his?

While you'll copy many of the things you observe while watching him masturbate to climax you can add a lot of zest by keeping a few things in mind:

Wet Is The Word

There's no more important element for the task at hand than lubrication. While *some* guys like shaking the steak without lube, most don't. Unlike your mouth or vagina, your hand is not self-moisturizing. Meaning, you're going to chafe his penis if you don't add lubrication. Fortunately, the market is flooded with ways to keep your guy's manhood moist. Not all lubricants are equal during stroke sessions. Here's a breakdown of how the different options stack up:

Oil-Based

There's a reason Vaseline is as important to teenage boys as acne cream. Sure, you and your guy may think that you're too grown and sexy for a such a juvenile sex tool, but Vaseline and other oil-based lubes remain the gold standard for masturbation and hand jobs. They are thicker than other types of lube, creating an ideal coating over the dick rather dripping off, and they stay wet longer.

It's almost as if oil-based lubes were made specifically for male masturbation, as they're not something you would want to taste during oral sex, and they are generally considered unsafe for intercourse because they can damage latex. Another downside is that they can be harder to clean off of skin or fabric, but hey, club soda wasn't just made for mixing drinks. Read the label on the bottle. It says, "Great for removing cum stains."

I kid. Oil-based lubes are also the most affordable type of lube. You can virtually get a keg of petroleum jelly for under $10, and price is not factor you want to overlook with something as potentially high-volume as hand jobs.

Silicone-Based

One of the most significant technological advance-ments around the turn of the century was not the Internet, but rather the emergence of silicone-based lubes. They have a thinner texture than their oil-based counterparts, but contain much of the same effectiveness, and without the corrosive qualities that make them unsafe for intercourse. Silicone-based lubes don't absorb into the skin or evaporate into the air, meaning they last for quite awhile without having to re-apply them.

Like their oil-based counterparts, silicone-based lubes complicate the cleanup process. Getting them off fabric is like getting a guy off after a cocaine binge—nearly impossible, so lay a towel down to protect the sheets.

Water-Based

The most common type of lube on the market, they are generally the most suitable for sex. However, water-based lubes don't apply as evenly as oil-based lubes, which can result in "dry zones" along the dick

—unmoistened pockets of flesh that make your fingers "snag" the penis rather than glide across it. This, of course, will make him about as happy as a supermodel with blocked nostrils. Water-based lubes are also notoriously quick to dry, meaning you'll have to regularly squirt more on the penis to keep it wet and comfortable.

Organic

Wait, vegan lubes? Actually, there's a budding market for health-conscious hand strokers, as aloe, coconut oil, and honeybee lubes gain popularity. These varieties are ideal for folks with sensitive skin, or anyone who just wants to avoid chemicals during sex. The flavors and all-natural qualities of these lubes make them highly compatible with oral sex, and most are gluten-free.

However, many organic lubes absorb quickly into the skin, which means you'll be reapplying frequently during an extended hand job session.

Saliva

Nothing's hotter for a man than a woman who uses her natural juices to lube her man's dick, and there should be plenty of saliva already slathered on the penis if you're transitioning from oral sex to a hand job. But there's also no type of lube more ineffective for jacking off, since saliva evaporates after a few strokes. So unless your mouth is a faucet that can produce a consistent stream of moisture, you'll want to use something stronger than saliva when giving your guy a hand job.

What Properties To Look For In A Lube

I've described the main categories of lubes, but picking the right one is like picking the right partner—you want something that goes down easy, isn't smelly or hard to get off you. I've personally tried what some experts call "the best lubes" and hated them, so there's no point in telling you which lube I like best. You're better off test-driving the different brands and seeing for yourself. Here's what to look for:

Your grip should be firm but with enough "slack" for your hand to glide up and down his erect penis.

Texture & Smoothness: You don't want your personal lubricant to be sticky or tacky. You want your lube to be as slippery as your boyfriend when he's confronted with the strange panties you found in the back of his truck.

Dryness: Did the lube disappear after the first few strokes —like the commitment-phobe you dated last year? Or did it stick around like that guy last night that couldn't take a hint?

Type of Container: It may sound stupid to use this as a criteria but if it takes two hands to squeeze out a few drops it ain't worth it. You want the thing to be so easy you can open it with your feet. I'd stay away from jars and tubs –

they tend to collect pubic hair—a double-yuck in anybody's book.

Wash-off Factor: If you're looking for convenience, forget about oil-based lubes like Vaseline, baby oil or Crisco. While they may feel good, they destroy condoms and they're harder to get off the sheets than a visiting cousin.

Taste & Smell: Believe me it's important. Do you really want to use a lube that smells like the last pork chop in the butcher shop?

How Long It Lasts: You don't want a "premature ejaculating" lube. Meaning, three strokes and it's over. You want a long lasting lube so you don't have to keep re-applying it.

Irritation Factor: The two ingredients that cause most skin irritations are Nonoxynol-9 and glycerin (a form of sugar that makes lubes taste sweet). So, if either of you have sensitive skin use lubes made out of botanical ingredients.

Temperature: Some of the newer lubes create heat or cold when you rub it on. Like some of the guys we've all taken home, they can give you heat stroke or freezer burns.

A Vast Right-Hand Conspiracy

Your man's love life in the early years was like a gas station —strictly self-service, so his body is trained to respond to a certain type of speed, pressure and rhythm. It's always better to ask or watch him "punch the monkey" so you can get a better sense of what he likes. Still, these tips will fill in the blanks:

Grip

Both your hand and your man's penis have unique shapes to them so you'll want to explore different types of grips to see which ones are the most compatible and effective, both in terms of positioning, and in the tightness of your grip. Your grip should be firm but with enough "slack" for your hand to glide up and down his pole. And while you'll want the full area of your hand for most of the stroking, it's good to mix it up with by turning your thumb and index finger into an O-ring and stroking the upper third of his shame digit. One caveat: Never grab the penis like you're the calloused foreman of a construction company greeting the new recruits. Start by gently touching the contours of his dick and balls with the tops of your fingers and gradually tighten the grip.

Rhythm

Don't start pumping him like a heaving piston. Remember what I said earlier in the book: *Gradually slow to gradually fast.* Gently rub his cock with your hands, making it as hard as possible before you actually start pumping. Tip: Pumping a flaccid or not quite hard penis hurts! ALWAYS start out gently and build a rhythm.

While it's safe to mimic the rhythm of oral sex or inter-course, a hand job usually requires a bit more variety in the pacing of strokes. Sometimes it should be slow and long, other times fast and staccato. Your guy has a bit of "muscle memory" when it comes to jacking off, and so most penises have a specific pace of stroking needed to keep the party going and trigger a climax. You'll need to test drive his dick with your hand several times before you figure out the speed limit.

Boobs

Purists might argue that a hand job should involve nothing but fingers and palms, but let me tell you something about purists—they have boring sex. There's no reason you shouldn't turn a hand job into a boob job ("Tittie fucking!"). It's a great visual stimulant and adds a little flair to the up and downs.

Dirty Talk

Given that the pleasure of a hand job is entirely familiar to your man, it's not as naturally stimulating as more infrequent types of sex. His mind will reflexively shift into fantasy mode to help him reach orgasm, because that's what its been doing since he first discovered jacking off. Fuel his fantasies and arouse him with a little kinky conversation while you stroke him, especially about how the rest of your body is so jealous of your hand at that moment. Dirty talk will also keep the attention on you, as his instinct will be to re-visualize the PornHub scene he watched on his cell phone while jacking off in the employee restroom.

But really, I say that with love.

Don't Forget The Balls!

Women always forget the balls! Don't be one of them. Your man's penis may seem like a handful, but it's not the only part of his anatomy that should be massaged during a hand job. Be sure to play with his balls while you're stroking him, juggling them in your fingers, tickling the seam down the middle, stretching (gently!) the scrotum away from the penis, and raising them to the base of the shaft as if your fingers were a cock ring. You can also turn your digits into a tiny dildo, massaging his taint area to stimulate his prostate, which will increase his arousal and later, his ejaculation.

Now that we've covered the basics of handling your man, let's beef up your resume by expanding your (hand) job skills. Here are 10 of the most tested-and-approved methods for milking your man.

STOP! How Are YOU Doing?

Did you remember to check in and ask yourself what you need to make this hotter? The question is simple and it comes in many varieties: "How can I get more physical, emotional and sexual pleasure out of what I'm doing?" If it's to slow down so you can take a better look at his hard cock, then slow down. Would it turn you on to do it in front of a mirror? Then find one. Remember, you are there to please him *through your pleasure.*

Ol' Faithful

The most elementary hand job involves grasping your man's shaft with one hand while cupping his balls with the other. Guide your up-and-down strokes with your wrists, not your arm. Do this: Stick your arm straight out in front of you with your thumbnail facing the ceiling and your hand shaped like it's gripping your partner's member. Now keep your wrist still and move your arm up and down in exaggerated motions. Got it? Okay, now keep your arm still and move your wrist up and down. Great. Now, keep moving your wrist up and down and move your arm with it *slightly*. THIS is the perfect way to stroke him—a lot of wrist and very little arm. Your stroking should span from the base of the penis to just above the ridge of the head. The contact between your hand and your man's head will make him tingle, but be sure that your hand is not passing the ridge with abrasive force. Massage and tickle his balls while you stroke in order to get the semen-producing parts of his penis fully operating, and soon he'll be shooting out his magic potion.

Corkscrew

Make a ring with your thumb and index finger and position your hand at the base of your man's shaft, then use your other hand to make a similar ring around the head of the penis. Now bring those two rings together toward the middle of his shaft, twisting in opposite directions, using your wrist and elbows to maximize torque.

Launch & Orbit

Send your man into outer space with this technique, which uses two types of motion to help him lift off. Use your dominant hand to grasp the shaft and stroke it in your regular style (the launch), then place the other hand, palm open, atop the head of the penis and begin massaging it in a circular motion (the orbit). It might take some practice for you to master the harmony of the up-and-down and circular stimulation. It's a little like patting your head and massaging your belly in circles—it takes a minute or two to get it right, but it'll be well worth it when you see the look on his face.

Doggy Style

One of the ways to add novelty to an activity your man is intimately familiar with is to offer a technique that he can't fully enjoy by himself. Have him get on his knees in front of you, then pull his dick in between his spread thighs and begin stroking. The position accelerates blood flow to the penis, and gives your man a new sensation from what he is used to. It also gives you easy access to his taint and butt hole so you can amp up his orgasm.

Hand As Vagina

Here's a technique that varies from his solo stroke sessions. Pretend your hands are a telescope and look through them. Keep your hands in that position and lower them to crotch level. Now have him penetrate your hand-created faux-vagina. Essentially, all you're doing is keeping your hands still while he pumps his way to satisfaction—talk about an easy day's work!

Bookends

For this method, your hands are flattened on either side of his penis with your fingers pointing up. Pretend your hands are bookends propping up the best seller between them. Now move them up and down in parallel motion. Vary it by having the hands go in opposite directions. Vary it even further by turning the "bookends" on their side, where your thumbs are positioned toward the head and your pinkies toward his pubic hair.

Fire Starter

This technique is similar to Bookends in that both of your hands are flattened on either side of your man's penis, but with your fingers parallel to the floor. Instead of moving your hands in unison, alternate directions. Imagine you're warming your hand up, or rubbing kindle to start a fire, then let his cum douse the flames!

Knob Twister

Grip one of your hands around the base of your man's penis, and keep it stationary to help blood concentrate in the shaft and head. Use your other hand to gently grip the head, then begin twisting this hand (make sure it's lubed!) as if you were turning a door knob, opening an erotic euphoria that your man won't want to step out of.

V-Spot Pinch

Again, gripping the base of your man's dick with one hand, use the other to trace the underside of his shaft until you get to the V-Spot and begin tickling it. Next, form a ring with your thumb and index finger to twist circles around this super sensitive area. After stimulating the V-Spot for a few seconds with this motion, remove the ring from around the head, and begin *gently* pinching the V-Spot, rubbing it in soft circles.

Bottomless Pit

Turn your hands into an infinite love tunnel with this technique, in which you grip the top of your man's penis with one hand and slide it down the shaft. Before his head is fully exposed, use your other hand to repeat this same motion, and continue "stacking" your fists on his dick so that it feels like your man is penetrating a bottomless cavern. You can also reverse this technique, with the hands moving upward from the base to the head, giving your man the sensation that all of the life is about to be drained from him.

Now that you've tickled his pickle are you brave enough to toss his salad? Let's set the table and see if you're game.

Chapter Thirteen

Toss That Salad!
The Other Oral Sex

Given all the sausage we've binged on, it's time for a little lighter fare. Let's toss some salad! Now, I know some of you are thinking, "Whoa! I just lost my appetite!" But there's no reason to be queasy about butt-licking, commonly known as "rimming" or analingus. As long as he's clean you're not going to run into any poop chute stragglers or inhale odors that would spring the coil off a wall clock.

Your nervousness about the ick factor can be wiped away with a good shower. His ambivalence about getting his anus stimulated might take a conversation or two. First, I seriously doubt any woman has proposed it to him. Second, he probably thinks it doing it will make him gayer than a box of kittens. But enjoying ass play only makes you gay if your partner is a man. If it's a woman it simply makes you adventurous.

As undignified as it may seem on the surface, licking your man's butt hole flips the power dynamic to your favor, as the receiving partner turns submissive and the one doing the licking has all of the control.

The shared vulnerability in performing analingus increases

trust and enhances intimacy. He is letting you do things he's probably never let another woman do and you're exploring parts unknown. Both of you are vulnerable and that's why a shared experience like this can build intimacy. To avoid long-term emotional trauma, take your time initiating ana-lingus, and pay attention to what arouses your man and what alarms him. But be bold, as the final frontier of oral sex requires us to stray away from a guy's frontal region and explore the great beyond.

Bathing The Booty

It goes without saying that hygiene is of utmost importance to rimming, both in terms of safety and your comfort. You definitely don't want any bacon bits in this tossed salad! A human's rectum is covered in millions of germs, most of which are benign or serve beneficial purposes (such as preventing leakage or odor), but some of which—including E. coli and salmonella—can lead to, um, food poisoning. While it's healthiest to perform analingus using some form of dam (such as Saran Wrap), thoroughly washing the anus usually makes it safe enough for oral play. Your man doesn't have to scrub his butt with bleach or ammonia, but at the very least he should hit the showers and scrub the area with soap.

Full Steam Ahead Or Talk First?

There's a certain genius in surprising your partner with an adventurous romp but there are certain precautions you might want to entertain with this one. If you want to surprise him, make sure it's a night you're certain he's taken a shower and hasn't eaten a broccoli and bean salad. He may be clean but you don't want the breeze from his farts blowing hair in your eyes. If you want the element of surprise but are worried about his cleanliness, then take a bath together—it'll give you more confidence.

Your other option is to talk and tell him what you want to do: "Honey, I want to lick and kiss parts of you that I'm pretty sure no one's kissed." That will either bring up an erection or an alarm. Either way, the path forward is set.

Pleasure the 'P-Zone'

Before we dive into the dark abyss of analingus, we're going to spend some time frolicking in the entire pelvic zone (the "tain't," the back of his scrotum sack, and of course, his sphincter). This "P-Zone" is rarely stimulated by men themselves, let alone by their partners. It's very likely that you could be the first human to chart your man's pelvic zone and the unfamiliar sensations that rush through him will no doubt have his eyes rolling to the back of his head.

While you're licking your man's balls, take a detour to the right or left and begin licking the inner crevice of his thigh (behind and adjacent to his balls). It's likely he will flinch and squirm from the pleasure as in some men it feels ticklish. Brace yourself for his physical reaction and stay focused on taming him with your tongue. Reduce the tickling sensation by flattening your tongue to cover more area and going slowly so that your man's insecurities are replaced with comforting pleasure. You want him to enjoy this not flail in self-defense.

The inner pelvis is laced with connective penile tissue, directly linking it with your man's sexual nerve centers. This also means that it is extremely delicate and so you should make sure you don't apply too much pressure with your kissing.

The P-Zone offers a friendly region where you can practice and simulate your technique for eating your man's anus. Your tongue remains the most vital tool in this process, and it should be constantly dabbing, swiping and circling the inner pelvis, either by itself or in conjunction with the lips. You'll also be able to give a literal "blowjob," as this area is highly receptive to stimulation provided by a stream of air from your pursed lips. Remember to be fair and give equal attention to both sides of your man's pelvic region, stopping to show some love to the balls during the transition.

The P-Zone is an often uncharted paradise of pleasure, brimming with nerve endings, blood vessels and tissue that connects it to the penis. In fact, doctors who were research-ing ways to reconstruct a California man's penis after it was severed by his wife (talk about an awful blowjob!) consi-dered using a graft from the inner thigh to build a replace-ment penis, since the arteries and nerves were similar enough to the penis to allow him to be sexually functional.

Taste the Taint

As we discussed in the first chapter of this book, the taint is loaded with nerve endings, and serves as an outer access point to a man's prostate. Spread and slightly elevate your man's legs to allow you to tongue his taint, mimicking the motions he makes when he's eating you out—sucking with your lips, poking it with your tongue, and lavishing it with lascivious licks.

Eroticize the Air

Now you're ready to flip him onto his stomach and prepare his ass to be feasted upon. If you're still a little nervous about diving in face-first, the good news is that the first stage of analingus requires very little from you, as you can let nature work its magic. The butt hole is such a sensitive area that simply exposing it to surrounding air stimulates it. Just spread your man's butt cheeks and expose the rectum to the air and it will provide a slight tingling that signals more pleasure is on the way. Enhance this sensation by blowing air through your pursed lips—both by hitting the "bullseye" of the rectum, and circling the outer rim.

Seduce the Booty

To increase both you and your man's comfort, incorporate some anal foreplay before you begin penetrating his butt hole with your tongue. The term "Kiss my ass" usually has a negative connotation, but in this scenario it's a tender gesture of affection that can relax both of you. Cover his butt cheeks with a variety of kisses—tiny pecks, puckered smooches and full-throated French kisses—and allow the intimacy to alleviate anxiety. Massaging your man's butt cheeks is also a great way to release any stress he may be feeling and prime his sphincter for the massage your tongue is about to deliver.

Lost Lips

The rectum, or the outer ring of the butt hole, is made of tissue that is remarkably similar to the type found in our lips, and it responds to stimulation in much the same way. So don't look at it as if you're licking a guy's butt hole, but rather discovering a set of lost lips for you to make out with!

The Backside Buffet

Alright, enough with the appetizers, it's time to dig in for the main course! Think about what feels good when he's going down on your vagina then try to recreate techniques that bring you pleasure. Here's a little more specific guidance for how to make love to your man's butt with your mouth.

—**Tongue:** As you should expect by now, your tongue takes the steering wheel during analingus (hence, "rimming," where you circle the rectum with the tip of your tongue). Along with orbiting the outer ring of your guy's butt hole, flatten your tongue and take broad licks, lapping his ass up like it's an ice cream cone. Once you've been making out with the butt hole for a while, take the action to second base by massaging the rectum: Make your tongue firm and use the tip to knead the rectum's soft tissue. As you and your man get more heated and uninhibited, try penetrating the rectum with your tongue, your firm but malleable flesh seeping into his tight crevice.

—**Lips:** Mind-blowing analingus starts with a tight seal, so once your tongue makes contact with the rectum, open your mouth wide and use your lips to form a sort of tent over the butt hole. Your lips will seal in the warmth and produce saliva as your tongue massages his hole. Release the seal and use your lips to more thoroughly toss his salad —kissing his butt lips, gently sucking his rectum and blowing air on his wet hole.

—**Teeth:** When it comes to the rectum, you want to adopt the same rule about incisors we talked about earlier: Do. Not. Ever. But your teeth can still play an active part in analingus, gently gnawing and biting on your man's butt cheeks, especially the area above the hole, in the inner upper crack.

Mirror, Mirror

Guess what? Even though you and I have never met, I can tell you something about yourself: You've got a butt hole, too! Now, the law of sexual reciprocity is understood to mean "Tit for THAT." He goes down on you, you go down on him. He wants you to do something special you might not be crazy about; you ask for the same.

HOWEVER.

You should not call on the law of reciprocity too quickly in this case. When you're done giving your man a rim job, you shouldn't wipe your mouth and say, "My turn!" Especially if he didn't ask for it. Be a little more diplomatic. Better to invite than to expect ("Do you want to try it on me?").

Analingus is an act that while extremely pleasurable, carries a whole lot of baggage.

Still, the rectum is the only part of sexual anatomy possessed by both men and women. This gives you a rare opportunity for pure reciprocation and the chance to learn new techniques from one another.

Okay, since the start of this book you've learned every variation of the No Pants Dance, right? Not quite. There's one thing you've probably never tried and something only the most adventurous men would allow you to do. So wet your fingers. I'm not saying that just so it'll help you turn this page.

Chapter Fourteen

For WILD Couples Only! Combining BlowJobs With Prostate Massage

If you want your partner to experience a seismic orgasm that would register on a Pacific Rim Richter scale, then massage his prostate while you're blowing him. It would require you to penetrate his rectum with a lubed-up finger and stimulate his prostate gland.

There's just one problem. Three actually: Gay, gay, gay!

He will most likely perceive you finger-banging his bum as a violation of his masculinity. What's next? he'll ask. Designing the Macy's Christmas window? Figure skating? Cock-flavored lollipops? We'll talk about the best way of convincing him later. First, as the gays like to say when they're in a tight spot, "Let me back up."

Let's talk a little more about the prostate before we tackle whatever "gay panic" he might experience. The prostate is a walnut-sized gland located between the bladder and the penis (just in front of the rectum). It produces fluid that nourishes and protects sperm. During orgasm it squeezes this fluid into the urethra where it mixes with sperm and comes out as that whitish semen many of us think of as the nectar of the Gods.

Obviously, the prostate is crucial to a male's experience of orgasm. Ask your partner about his experience with "ejaculatory inevitability"—the point when he's about to come and he feels it deep inside before anything comes out. The vas deferens, seminal vesicles and the prostate generate that feeling.

If the prostate plays such a critical part of a man's orgasm, it makes sense that stimulating it is going to dramatically heighten the pleasure of an orgasm. That's not a gay fact; it's a male fact. Stimulating your prostate with a finger (yours or your partner's) or an object doesn't make you gay. Not that there's anything wrong with that (I should know!). Being anally penetrated doesn't mean you're so far in the closet you found Christmas presents or ran into the lion in Narnia. It simply means you discovered a way to make your orgasms more pleasurable.

To show you how "not gay" prostate stimulation is, consider the poor schmucks who have prostatitis, an inflammation of the prostate. The most effective treatment is to "milk" the prostate by stimulating it with a finger. Doctors, mostly male, do it 2 or 3 times week for their male patients.

So, if it isn't "gay" for a male doctor to insert his finger into another man's bum and stimulate his prostate then why is it gay to have a girlfriend or wife do it?

Besides, I can almost guarantee your partner has had

another man inside his ass and he didn't consider it gay. *Guarantee it.* Has he ever had a physical? Then he's had a man's hands up his ass. It's the only way to conduct a prostate exam.

A recent survey showed that 80% of women would perform a prostate massage if asked by their partner, so clearly the objection is not coming from women. It's coming from men who fear being perceived as a 'mo if they wander down that path.

What a crock. Even if your partner ends up loving getting his prostate stimulated, even if he wanted to put objects up there to get a bigger bang, that still wouldn't make him gay. Even if he wanted a dick up there it wouldn't make him gay.

Massaging his prostate has the potential of giving him an explosively pleasurable —and sometimes spontaneous—orgasm.

Wait, what? You heard me. Lea DeLaria, my favorite lesbian comic, explains it best. She once said, *"I don't know why people say lesbians don't like dick. We love dick! We just don't like them on men."*

My point is that even if your heterosexual partner wanted a dick up his ass, he wouldn't want it hanging off a man. He'd want it hanging off you! He'd want you to buy a strap-on dildo and have at him.

Dorothy, You're Not In Ken's Ass Anymore

Now that we've gotten his gay panic situation handled (hopefully), let's get back to putting more ohhhhs in his orgasms. Stimulating the prostate in just the right way can create enormous sexual excitement. In some men, simply stroking the prostate can make them spontaneously orgasm.

The biggest obstacle to massaging the prostate is getting past the two sphincters that guard the goods inside.

Everybody Has Two Sphincters.

The two sphincters are distinct but overlapping bands of muscle tissue. And while they serve the exact same function (regulating grand openings and final close-outs) they go about it in different ways. You are most familiar with the external sphincter because you can order it to tighten and release. Here, try it. Squinch your starfish by using the muscles to stop yourself from peeing. Got it? Tighten, release, tighten, release. Now, this time with feeling! Tighten, release! Tighten, release!

Now do five fast tightens. Get it? You can boss that part of your butt around. Feel like taking a crap but there's no bathroom around? No problem. You can will your external sphincter not to open. At least for a while.

But the internal sphincter? You can't tell it to do shit. And I mean that in every sense of the word. You are not its boss. Like your blood pressure and heartbeat, you cannot directly control it.

Do this: Put your hands in front of you as if you're praying. Now intertwine your fingers down to the webbing and press your palms together as tight as you can. Now keep everything connected and completely relax both hands. Notice the small opening between the side of your thumb and your index finger? This is the opening to your anus. If somebody tried to poke their finger through that opening it would feel snug but it'd go in pretty easy.

Now tighten both hands as hard as you can. The left hand is the internal sphincter you cannot directly control. The right hand is the external sphincter you can. Keeping the left hand tight as a drum, completely relax your right hand. Your right hand (external sphincter) is relaxed so a *slight* opening was created. But your left hand (internal sphincter) is so tight that it won't let a poking finger through very easily.

Welcome to anal play's first dilemma: The left hand doesn't know what the right hand is doing. Or more accurately, the left hand doesn't *care* what the right hand is doing. The internal and external sphincters can and often do work independently of each other. In order to make penetration smooth and effortless *both* sphincters have to get on the same page.

So!

In order to massage the prostate, you have to get your partner to relax *both* his sphincters. Here's how:

Step 1: Put lube on your middle finger and on his anal opening.

Step 2: Gently press your finger against the anal opening.

Do not insert. Just keep your finger pressed gently but firmly on the opening to his anus. Stay here for a few moments and let your finger feel what's happening to his external sphincter. Make sure, however, that you're pressing on, not just touching, the sphincter. Again, press but don't insert.

Step 3: Have him inhale to a count of four while he tightens his sphincter as hard as he can.

Keep your finger gently pressed, but not inserting, into his clenched anus. Have him keep a steady count to four until he gets to the end of the inhale. Pause for a second and...

Step 4: Have him relax his sphincter as he exhales to a count of six.

You are not pushing your finger in during the exhale—*his sphincter is relaxing onto the finger,* which is gently but firmly placed against it. Only draw in as far as the exhale/relaxation allows. If he feels discomfort or pain back off. Remember, he should <u>never</u> feel pain. Discomfort maybe, but pain? No. It's a signal you're doing it wrong—you're either pressing too hard or going in too fast.

How much of your finger got drawn in? An inch? One eighth of an inch? It doesn't matter. What matters is that you just experienced the secret to finger-banging without pain:

You don't insert a finger into your rectum;
you relax onto it.

This is an important concept to understand and apply. Inserting an object into the anal canal guarantees a tightening of the sphincter muscles. But relaxing onto it guarantees a loosening of them. Do this: Palm down, clench your left fist tight, tight, tight. Now try to force the index finger of your right hand into your clenched fist. Make it a battle. Notice the clenched fist will win. Now, press the index finger gently but firmly against the clenched fist without trying to force it in. Inhale to a count of four as you clench the fist as tight as you can. Now, loosen the clenched fist as you exhale to a count of six. Notice how a bit of your finger went in without actually having to forcefully insert it? This concept works with your fist and it works with your (and his) sphincter muscles. Again:

Don't insert a finger into his butt;
allow his butt to draw it in.

This technique is so effective because it is working with anatomy, not against it. A relaxed sphincter releases *downward*. When it tightens, it contracts *upward*, drawing in whatever it was relaxed onto. This release-downward/contract-upward process facilitates an interesting anatomical phenomenon: A small vacuum that literally sucks a part of the finger in.

His body will start to understand (and react favorably) to the rhythm—inhale to tighten, exhale to loosen. Inhale to tighten, exhale to loosen. Once again:

*You are not inserting your finger;
you are letting his sphincter draw it in.*

Now that you have your finger up his ass, let's move on.

Step 5: Let His Sphincter Get Used To The Presence Of Your Finger.

Once you draw your finger in (no matter how little), keep it there without moving. As his anus realizes it's not under attack you will feel the sphincter muscles relaxing further. If you really pay attention you'll feel both sphincters. They feel like two separate rings with about a quarter of an inch of flesh between them. Have him squeeze and relax his anus. Notice that the external sphincter relaxes on command while the internal sphincter does not. You can actually feel it tightening and relaxing spontaneously in pulses, as if it had a mind of its own. Don't do anything, just notice it.

Keep your finger in there long enough and you'll physically feel the internal sphincter—the one that does not obey conscious commands—relax around your finger. Feel it? You just experienced a great lesson: If you're patient enough the muscles you can't consciously control will unconsciously release. It's a simple law of physics. Do this: Clench your fist as hard as you can. Keep it tightly clenched as long as you can. You'll notice that after a period of time the muscle simply gives out. It cannot sustain the same level of tension forever. This brings us to another key concept in pain-free finger-banging:

His internal sphincter will relax if he lets it let go.

This requires patience, of course. But you saw "first hand" in the example above how the internal sphincter released on its own if you stayed still long enough. Okay, let's keep going. At this point his sphincter muscles should be so used to the inserted finger that he literally can't feel much of anything.

Step 6: Lather. Rinse. Repeat.
Repeat steps 1-6 until his sphincter muscles have drawn in your entire finger or you simply want to stop because you don't want to miss the next episode of Family Guy.

Now that we've gotten your whole finger inside his butt without causing pain, let's look for the prostate!

Step 1: Gently Probe The Anal Wall Upwards Towards His Navel.
The prostate is located behind the anal wall in the direction of his belly button (two to four inches from the sphincter). Be careful! The prostate is very sensitive. Do not poke and prod. Caress and stroke. Press gently. Use feather-light touches. You're looking for a walnut-sized fleshy ball hiding behind the anal wall. Finding it is a little like playing hide-and-seek, only you're using your finger rather than your eyes.

It's astounding to feel his prostate thicken and grow inside the anal wall as he get closer to orgasm. It gives you a fascinating glimpse into male sexual response.

Step 2: Find And Trace The Contours Of The Prostate.

Once you locate it, trace your finger around the gland. Take a tour. Notice where it is. Make a mental note of how far in (and up) you had to go so that you can use this memory as a GPS for the next time you do it. Ask him how stroking his prostate feels. Good, bad? Pleasurable? Ambivalent?

Can't Find His Prostate Or Not Sure If You Have?

The easiest way to find his prostate is to make sure he's sexually aroused. His penis isn't the only thing that gets full and erect when he gets excited—so does the prostate. So much so that it bulges into the anal wall, making it very easy to find. During arousal the prostate fills with semen fluid. The closer he gets to orgasm the firmer the prostate becomes and the easier it is to find and stroke.

You can also have him try different positions. For example, some people have better luck lying on their left side and putting their right hand behind their back while bending the knee of the top leg.

fingers aren't long enough. The prostate lies two to four inches into his rectum (towards his belly button). If his prostate is positioned higher than average and/or your fingers are shorter than average it can get a little tricky. Try a commercial prostate massager like Aneros. It's shaped to match the form of the anus.

Step 3: Massage The Prostate.

You need to exert firm pressure without pushing too hard. Firm but comfortable is your goal. Start at the top of the prostate and slowly push down toward the center. Then go back up. Then start at the bottom and slowly push upwards toward the center. Experiment with different directions to get different sensations. There's no right or wrong way to find out what he likes. Be curious and try anything as long as you do it slowly, with care. The prostate actually has two lobes. If you can detect each lobe you can take turns massaging them. Don't be surprised if a couple of drops of fluid come out of his penis, even if it's not erect. This is what many doctors do to "milk" the prostate and relieve pressure in patients with enlarged prostates.

Step 4: Massage The Prostate While He Masturbates.

He may or may not get an erection while you're exploring the prostate. It's now time for him to purposefully get one. While you can blow him or fondle him with your hands, it's best that he masturbate this first time so you can concentrate on the lay of the land. Massage the prostate as he masturbates to climax. Get ready for an awesome experience: As he gets close to coming you'll feel his prostate SWELL inside his body and as he ejaculates you'll feel his entire rectal area—sphincters and all—rhythmically contracting as he ejaculates. It's a phenomenal feeling to experience his orgasm from the inside out.

You Can Do It Without Finger Penetration

You can also try a more indirect route to stimulating his prostate—finding the pressure point on the perineum directly below the prostate. Do this: Put your index and middle fingers together and gently press the fingertips on the area between his anus and the scrotum. Again, southerners call this area "The Tain't" because it "tain't your ass and it tain't your balls."

Start at the boundary of his sphincter and *gently* press up. Move an 1/8 of an inch toward your scrotum and press up. Keep going and you will eventually find the sweet spot— generally, it's the most sensitive spot in a most sensitive area. Try different pressures and find the touch that he like best.

Stellar Tip! Squeeze More Semen Out Of Him Than Even He Knew He Had

You can wring the last bit of semen out of his ejaculation by doing the following: Right after he ejaculates, press your fingers upward on the t'aint, starting at the edge of his sphincter and glide them firmly (but gently) toward the scrotum. As you reach the scrotum, clasp the base of his penis and squeeze up to the head. You are basically squeezing the last bit of toothpaste out of the tube. Start at the base (the area just above your sphincter) and keep squeezing until you reach the opening (the tip of the urethra). You'll see extra semen come out that you—and he—didn't know he had in him. If he's a "dripper" after he ejaculates (continues to drip semen even after his penis goes soft) this will completely eliminate it.

I promise you the vast majority of men have never done this. His eyes will widen in shock when he sees you squeeze more semen out. Oh, and it also feels great!

Was It Good For Him?

Some guys find prostate stimulation unbelievably pleasurable while other guys find it extremely annoying. Some men only like it after a certain point of sexual arousal while others like it at any time. Still others don't care for it at all. Individuals vary widely. What causes ecstasy for some causes boredom in others.

It doesn't matter whether he likes prostate stimulation or not. What matters is that you guys had a wild adventure and experienced a process very few heterosexuals have. It is quite astounding to feel his prostate thicken and grow inside the anal wall as he get closer to orgasm. It gives you a fascinating glimpse into male sexual response and a sense of respect for the process the body goes through to deliver pleasure.

Okay, you've made it to the end. Or rather, his. Now it's time to wrap up and review everything you've learned.

Chapter Fifteen

A Few Conclusions To Hammer In

I do enjoy the sensation of feeling it in my mouth; when poked it's hard and firm but the texture is silky smooth. It's like licking a popsicle made of steel but kept in a taut silk bag.

—K.

The traditional way of giving head—what I call the "selfless blowjob"—is a no-strings-attached gift to the man. It's giving without getting and it will eventually end up making you feel used and sexually bored. But in "selfish" blowjobs pleasure is distributed evenly and in many ways, tilted to your favor.

Selfish blowjobs require the giver to think of herself first and her partner second while aiming for mutual pleasure. It doesn't mean doing something your partner doesn't like just because you do. For example, it might bring you great pleasure to bite his dick with your back molars, but that would inconsistent with the concept of mutual pleasuring. Selfish blowjobs are not about denying your partner pleasure but in prioritizing yours. It's about finding the overlap between two parties, the sweet spot that allows the giver to get as much or more as the given.

Tune In So You Can Turn On

Have you ever seen a speaker tap a microphone that's obviously working and ask, "Is this thing on?" You need to do the same thing to your partner's dick—tap it and ask, "Am I turned on?" Because if you're not, you're never going to enjoy blowing him.

Get in touch with why you like masculinity's Main Representative and you will certainly start liking blowjobs. For most women, it's a curious mix of feeling powerful *and* submissive as described here:

"I love LOVE giving my fiancé head. I love the feeling of knowing that I'M in control, teasing him, knowing that it's all me that's making him curl his toes and go crazy from the teasing. I love hearing him moan as I do what I do, hearing him say I'm amazing, pulling my hair etc."

—*P.*

"I'm pretty submissive so the act of a blowjob ranges either from teasing him and watching him squirm to being dominated and deep throated. I've definitely come before while sucking someone with no stimulation so it's mostly a mental thing. At this point, I kind of

just love having a cock in my mouth, especially my SO's [significant other's] who I adore and who is always really mind blown by it (his ex didn't like giving oral)."

—L.

But attraction to power dynamics aren't the only reason to want his hardness in your mouth. It's also about the pleasure you get from seeing him in so much ecstasy that renders him incapable of thought. And because his erection is a symbol of his attraction for you, it makes sense that you would want to pleasure it. Its hard but silky sensation has a good "mouth feel" and having it there creates a tender after-it's-done intimacy.

Once you understand why you like penis, it's time to express that desire with your lips, tongue, throat and hands. But not just for him; for you. As I've said before, to truly give great head you have to see it as critical to your own sexual satisfaction. You have to see blowjobs as a principal way for you to pleasure *yourself*, not just him. If you don't, you'll see it as a chore, not a choice; a task not a turn-on.

Once you approach blowjobs with the idea that you are going to get as much or more pleasure than your partner, *then* you're ready to apply the techniques we've talked about in the book. If you can master the nine most important techniques below, everything else is just frosting on the cake (white and creamy!):

1. Your Mouth Has To Be Wetter Than A Cucumber At A Women's Prison

The wetter your mouth the better it'll feel to him and the easier it will be on your mouth, lips, tongue and throat. You'll slip, slide and glide easier and get more pleasure out of what you're doing. The fastest, most convenient way to produce more saliva while you're giving him head is to visualize biting into a lemon or to "gleek" – placing the tip of your tongue on the roof of your mouth for a few moments (it pools the saliva under your tongue).

2. Always Start Slow And Gradually Build Up

Apply the law of reciprocity—how would you want him to go down on you? You'd want a slow build. Think of an iron warming up, not a rocket taking off.

Everything should start gently and slowly (the grip, the pressure, the speed) and build toward a climax, with an emphasis on the journey, not the destination. Think of a giant roller coaster. You don't just get on it and jerk away at 60 MPH. It chugs slowly and inexorably toward the top and then...all hell breaks loose.

3. Don't Forget The Balls! Women Always Forget The Balls!

It's every guy's main complaint. The scrotum sack isn't there for decoration (if it were it'd look a lot prettier). It's a joy palace packed with sensitive nerve endings that can make the difference between him momentarily enjoying a blowjob and fantasizing about it for a month.

4. Use Your Hands As An Extension Of Your Mouth

After a few minutes of mouth-only action, you will drive him crazy if you add your hands to the mix. Mouths can't create the pressure or friction most guys need to maximize their pleasure (especially to ejaculate).

5. Use Your Tongue To French Kiss The Head Of His Penis

This is one of those "If you don't remember anything else" tips because the sensation is so extraordinary.

6. Make Some Noise

Sweet smacking sounds, squelchy, sloppy slurping and slovenly sucking are music to a man's ear. He'll put it on Spotify and mark it as his favorite playlist. Sex sounds are primal passion boosters; their power cannot be overstated.

7. Keep Him On Edge With The Peacock Technique

Use a "suspense and resolve" approach to build anticipation and create memorable experiences. Remember, it's not what you do to him. It's where you take him. And you can take him to the edge of space with a Tease-Lure-Escalate-Resolve model.

8. Keep The Same Rhythm When He's Close To Climaxing

There's such a thing as momentum during sex and you don't want to change anything when you sense it. If he starts approaching "ejaculatory inevitability," keep the same grip, pressure, speed, rhythm and moisture until he finishes completely. Do not change anything (unless he asks you to —and it's usually "Faster! Harder!") It's fine if you don't want to swallow or even get semen in your mouth—pull your mouth off his cock but keep going with your hands. It's also important for you to keep going until he has completely stopped coming. Better to have him pull you off than to leave him too early in his hour of need.

9. The Most Important Technique Of All!

There is one last technique and it's critical to an effective blowjob. Everything else we've talked about falls apart if you skip it. Let me re-introduce it by asking you to solve a riddle. But here's the thing—YOU CAN'T USE A CALCU-LATOR. Are you ready?

> You are driving a bus from London to Milford Haven in Wales. In London, 17 people get on the bus. In Reading, six people get off the bus and nine people get on. In Swindon, two people get off and four get on. In Cardiff, 11 people get off and 16 people get in. In Swansea, three people get off and five people get on. In Carmathen, six people get off and three get on. You then arrive at Milford Haven. What was the name of the bus driver?

It's YOU, silly. My point, and I really do have one, is that it's easy to lose yourself in an activity that requires you to pay attention to other people. You should approach a blowjob the way you approach a vibrator—by asking yourself how it can give you the most pleasure.

That means asking yourself a lot of questions throughout a blowjob session. Like, am I comfortable? Does this feel good to me? How can I make this feel even better? How can I enhance the physical sensations I'm experiencing? What can I do that will turn me on more?

And the most important question? It's for your partner: What can HE do to give you more pleasure?

Oh, Swell

When it comes to blowjobs you can go from "I don't want to do this" to "I don't want this to stop" by simply tuning in to what turns you on about a penis and learning techniques that give mutual pleasure. In fact, this is how you should approach any sex act.

You must see blowjobs as an effective way for you to pleasure yourself, not just him. Otherwise you'll see it as a task not a turn-on.

If you follow the instructions in this book you will be able to give such great blowjobs and get so much out of them you'll be tempted to try them on lots and lots of guys. But I'd like to offer a cautionary tale against doing it with inappropriate people. Meet my single friend, Doctor Judy. She could never give good head and she hated it at any rate. I coached her with the techniques in this book and she went from "Meh" to "Meow!" in a matter of weeks. She wanted to try her newfound skills on multiple partners but she worked 14-hour days at her practice, so she didn't have the opportunity to meet a lot of men.

Unfortunately, she ended up having sex with several of her patients. She tried to rationalize her behavior by reminding me that she was single, that her patients were single, that she wasn't the first doctor to sleep with her patients, and that nobody was harmed by the experiences. Finally, she asked for my advice.

I said, "Judy, *you're a vet.*"

My point, and I do have one, is a) Never take your male pets to Dr. Judy, and b) Don't take sex so seriously. The point is to have fun. Thank you for allowing me to help you build a better sex life.

Other Books By Michael Alvear

Read this remarkable guide and find out how to:

- Shut off the negative thoughts about your body before, during and after sex.

- Use techniques that will make you forget to "check" your thighs or worry about your partner seeing something that you're ashamed of.

- Stop panicking when your partner touches a body part you're self-conscious about.

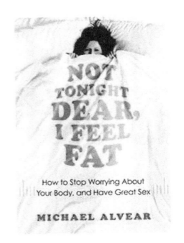

NOT TONIGHT DEAR, I FEEL FAT

How to Stop Worrying About Your Body, and Have Great Sex

MICHAEL ALVEAR

Available at bookstores everywhere.

- **Painlessly Reduce The Amount Of Food You're Eating.** Psychologists use Systematic Desensitization and Habituation to get people off Vicodin and Xanax. Imagine how well they work on chips and cookies.

- **Control Your Cravings With Delayed Gratification Techniques That Teach Discipline Without Suffering.** Based on famed psychologist Walter Mischel's "Marshmallow" experiments, they will painlessly help you master self-control and help you reach your diet and weight loss goals.

- **Eat Healthier Without Forcing Yourself To Eat What You Don't Like.** Use the "Nutrilicious" concept to make healthier choices without sacrificing taste or preferences.

"A wellness strategy that changes the way you think about food. Alvear's writing style and the structure of his book make for an easy read and, more importantly, easy use in daily life."

—*Kirkus Reviews*

Available at bookstores everywhere.

Made in the USA
Las Vegas, NV
13 February 2021

17800143R00142